THE PERSON IN THE WOMB

THE PERSON
IN THE WOMB

by N. J. Berrill

DODD, MEAD & COMPANY

NEW YORK

Library of Congress Catalog Card Number: 68-26153

Printed in the United States of America
by The Cornwall Press, Inc., Cornwall, N.Y.

Contents

THE PERSON IN THE WOMB

CHAPTER 1 *On Being Human*

Man is a relatively late comer on this aging earth. A poet has said that he is a spirit and symbols are his meat. He has also been called a large, naked biped with a big brain. In fact he is many things, depending on how narrow or broad or deep the point of view. He is an organism, in common with every other living thing upon this planet. Watery, sensitive, responsive and self-propagative. Above all, transient, with a beginning and an end, from which comes our joy of life and our despair. He is also a fish out of water, with bottled-up juices inside a dry skin, forever coping with the down-dragging force of gravity, levering himself along with muscles and bones. And he is a mammal, one among many. As such he, or more particularly, she is a reproductive device that produces young alive and requires sexual intercourse to start the process—setting the stage for family life.

Whatever man may be in the abstract and at large, he is first an individual, and the nature of this individual is the key to any understanding of mankind as a whole. For the human essence is expressed in the individual human life. In the development of a human being from a nearly invisible egg, there is truly a process of self-creation that continues through life. In certain ways it reflects the billion-year evolutionary process that brought it into being. The essence of man, however, is to a great extent a question of individual time. Something has happened during the period of human evolution to slow down individual human development, to stretch out the individual, so to speak, between the beginning and the end.

Infancy, childhood and adolescence now amount to nearly twenty years, the reproductive phase to thirty years or more, and the postreproductive period, for woman at least, to more than a quarter century. This last especially is unheard of in the rest of the animal kingdom. What has happened appears to be primarily a lengthening of the learning period from birth to puberty, a period when the young human can continually acquire new skills, including speech and communication generally, together with the transmitted experience of elders—in short, the period of educability, which has been the prime factor in the progressive ascendancy of human wits over a more or less hostile environment.

The individual human life, allowed to run its course, is still too short for time-conscious human beings. Yet for every one of us so blessed it is far more time than most creatures have individually enjoyed throughout life's long history. We who now look backward to the earth's beginning and forward to a certain but unpredictable future have much to consider, with so little time, yet so much of it and not all of it the same. What can a person do with his time, what does he need, what can he become, what molds him, how self-creative can he be? And, in the beginning, what makes him?

The human potential as a whole rests upon the nature and potential of the individual. The individual, however, combines universality with individuality. Like all of us, he is human. And like each of us, he is unique. Both aspects demand recognition. Our diversity is as precious as is our common humanity. No two humans are exactly alike. No one else is like oneself. Recognition of this gives a unique value to the person and also demands recognition of the uniqueness of others. Such is the basis for tolerance. Yet personality and individuality develop and must continue to develop, and are never something to be leveled off and destroyed. No one is perfect, no one is average, no one is normal. These are abstractions. Everyone possesses traits and abilities in different degrees. One person is superior in some traits, poor in others. Another person has a different assortment of deficiencies and superiorities. No one is average in every trait, no one is outstanding in all, no one deficient in all.

The scientific facts about each and every one of us should be comforting. Each of us probably excels in several desirable traits. According to Roger Williams, a humanist and physiologist,

Maybe it will be in rote memory, maybe in sense of pitch, in empathy, in appreciation of design, in word familiarity, in spatial imagery, in peripheral vision, in altruism, in sense of timing, in emotional strength, in orderliness, in loyalty or in any one or several of the dozens of traits which we possess. The realization of this should be of the greatest value to the individual, whether anyone else knows it or not, but if the realization is shared by others it can become a tremendous psychological boon. It puts the so-called average individual in a dignified position upon a pinnacle, in fact.

Every person needs to know, and to know as a child, that he is the only one of his kind and that his companions are each different in ways of their own and demand respect for what they are. He needs to know that whether his gifts are large or small they are his own, and that he sees the world around him in a somewhat different way than has ever been seen before. He should also know that when all minds are uncommon, the most uncommon may have by far the most to tell and that the greater the minds the greater the differences. Individually and collectively we are faced with the search for excellence, in awareness, in appreciation and in performance. Self-creation and self-fulfillment are the crying needs of every person. Quality of body, mind and spirit is paramount. If this be the goal for every man, it shows a narrow path, and it is doubtful whether a rampaging, voracious multibillion human herd can squeeze along it.

The person is sacrosanct, once the person has come into being. The person develops in the womb, not at once but belatedly, gradually and in a self-creative way. This is the most hazardous time of all. The process continues after

4

birth and for years is dependent on the total circumstances of life and love. It continues, or should continue, throughout maturity and age. Before birth there is little more than potential, no real actuality except for what might become. But with awakening at birth, the present and the future is upon us all. In body and mind and soul the human being reaches for new life, gathering all experience for the sake of being and of growth. Whatever or whoever tramples upon the spirit is evil. It is the human birthright to be born whole in body, brain and senses, to be nourished materially, emotionally and mentally and to stand in a world where there is space and beauty and where the essential dignity of the individual is known to all. And by the same token no child must be born without a hope, no woman must bear a child against her will and the sons of men must not overwhelm the earth.

CHAPTER 2 *To Be*

Every human being is a miracle of existence. Each has a past going back generation by generation, tissue from tissue, in an unbroken line for thousands of millions of years to the beginning of life on earth. Each individually begins with the development of a microscopic egg that is the outcome of an unforseeable chance meeting of a particular egg and a particular sperm, of one egg out of hundreds that might have ripened and descended to the womb and of one sperm out of millions that ascended to meet it. To be alive, in terms of chance, is far luckier than we know. Whether we enjoy it or not, whether our life be long or short, we who live are aware of self and of the world without and should be exultant. As Aldous Huxley once wrote,

A million million spermatozoa
        All of them alive
Out of their cataclysm but one poor Noah
        Dare hope to survive.

6

And among that billion minus one
Might have chanced to be
Shakespeare, another Newton, a new Donne—
But the One was Me.

Nature is wasteful, a gambler from the start who throws her seed to the winds of chance that a few may survive. In humans and other mammals, compared with most lower forms of life, the throw is under some control but chance still reigns. For humankind as well as others the question is: who lives and who does not, out of all the host of those who might have been or may be yet to come. Yet chance is now less blind than she used to be, in that we ourselves now influence the cast for better or for worse.

In a steady rhythm, at a particular time each month, in every woman during the thirty to forty years from menarche to menopause, a ripe egg leaves the ovary alternately of one side and the other and descends to the womb. It is a remarkably small beginning, a speck of protoplasm about one-quarter the size of a pinhead and just visible to the naked eye. Yet it has a force that can carry it through nearly a century of tumultuous existence and a capacity for growth and consumption that knows hardly any bounds, for in that speck lies the potential of the atomic bomb and a landing on the moon, of goodness and evil incarnate, of wit or witlessness. The force is there in every egg, the product unpredictable.

Before birth the ovaries of every female human baby contain nearly half a million cells, all of which are potential eggs. Yet for every one that ripens, between four and five thousand others become nurse cells forming a fluffy mass around the chosen one and giving it nourishment. Nothing is known concerning the nature of the choice, if choice it be. Later, during her fertile years, a woman liberates between three and four hundred fully grown, fertilizable eggs, one per month generally from thirteen years of age to forty-eight. But that is the number of eggs ovulated only if none are fertilized, for every conception suppresses the process of egg ripening and liberation for as long as pregnancy and nursing continue. On an average no more than three out of the three hundred or so chances for conception materialize as human beings of the next generation. Chance of another sort determines the choice.

Human eggs are small by almost any standard, and the three to four billion eggs that have yielded the present population of the earth could all have been stuffed into a single quart-size jar, a very small mass of living matter to be responsible for the rape of the earth that is now in progress. Yet all the spermatozoa that fertilized these eggs could have been compressed into a pill no larger than an aspirin, although here again nature deals in extraordinarily high numbers. Only a single sperm is needed for the fertilization of an egg, and only one sperm can be permitted to do so if fertilization is to be normal. Yet with every ejaculation by a healthy male, several hundred million spermatozoa are launched on the journey. Each one of us is accordingly the product of a chance meeting between one out of several hundred fully ripened eggs and one out of the several million sperm present at the time. Change anything at all, whether a night or a wiggle, and nothing would be the same.

Eggs must be fertilized. That is the general rule, although there are exceptions to any rule. An egg that has entered an oviduct on its way to the womb is launched on its course the moment a sperm hits its surface. Until that moment it has been sluggish, metabolically speaking, and the touch of the sperm is electrifying, both literally and chemically; a whole chain of actions and reactions is set in motion. And this seems to be one of nature's greatest obsessions, her need to produce fertilized eggs and to launch them upon their careers. It calls attention to the difference between the sex cells and why they should be so different. Perhaps the persisting debate concerning the equality of the sexes finds its ultimate roots in the nature of the sex cells as such. It is usually dangerous to probe too far, and the question that quickly arises is whether sex cells and, by implication, the males that bear them are really necessary. The male ego demands that the answer be yes, but the affirmative is less emphatic than it would be had the same question been put concerning the female. Why, then, are eggs and sperm so unlike, and what are their respective contributions to the organism-to-be?

Much of it is simply a division of labor, for it is always difficult to be a jack-of-all-trades and be an expert in all of them. The cell that is to develop into a new creature must first unite with another cell. Such has been the rule since time out of mind, whatever the underlying reasons may be, for not all of them concern development. They have to get together and they need substance enough at least to get development under way. So one kind stores reserves and is too fat to move—in short is an egg. And the other is motile, has very little substance and does what traveling there is to be done. It is a sperm. As such, eggs and sperm are remarkably similar throughout the animal kingdom, the sperm especially, for eggs do vary greatly in size and content. Wherever they may be, the eggs await their partners, whether the eggs be few and large, as in any bird or reptile, or small but produced in astronomical numbers to be carried by the ocean or equally small but few and retained in the womb of a mammal. As John Milton wrote some centuries ago, "they also serve who only stand and wait"; although many eggs are potentially self-sufficient, whereas all sperm are meaningless by themselves.

In general eggs must be produced in numbers sufficient to maintain the species from generation to generation, with a large margin of safety in an uncertain world. Sperm must be produced in numbers sufficient to find the eggs. A human egg is minute compared with a hen's egg or even with the relatively small eggs of frogs, yet it is a giant compared with sperm of any sort. In fact the sperm of every kind of living creature is truly microscopic, so that ten thousand may be placed side by side and not cover an inch. Human sperm are no exception. Each is driven forward by the lashing of its whiplike tail. Yet all such cells are so small that no matter how rapid the lashing of the tail may be the forward movement is very slow indeed in terms of distance to be covered. Consequently the chances of any particular sperm cell ever coming within striking distance of an egg are very slight, and even in the best circumstances enorm-

ous numbers of sperm are necessary to ensure that an egg
will be fertilized.

An egg, any egg, may be likened to a sleeping beauty.
All the potential of full and active life is there, needing
only the awakening kiss. Quite apart from size, the two
kinds of sex cells are far from being equal. Sperm cells for
instance can exist in an active state for merely a matter of
hours, although, massed in cool storage, they can survive
inactive for weeks or months. Given the opportunity, however, a sperm can make contact and penetrate an egg, stimulating the egg to begin development and also contribut-
ing sperm components to the makeup of the developing
system. The egg, on the other hand, under certain circumstances, can develop into a full-fledged organism without
any aid from a spermatozoan. Everything necessary for
such an event is present, and the egg system is all ready to
develop once its lethargy has been overcome.

The eggs of many kinds of lowly marine animals can be
made to develop without benefit of paternity by simply
adding an organic acid to the seawater. Frog eggs can be
made to develop by gently pricking the surface with a glass
needle dipped in lymph or even by raising the temperature
of the water around them. Admittedly they all develop into
males, which may be some consolation to human mascul-
inity, showing that spermatozoa do have a little to say at
least about sex in addition to giving the virgin egg a signal
to get up and go. In any beehive a proportion of bee eggs
develop spontaneously in this way, unfertilized, without
benefit of sperm, although only to give rise to drones that

do no work but merely contribute one of their number to a suicidal mating with a queen when the time arrives—playboys kept around for a single mating performance by only one of them. Virgin eggs *can* develop without help or contribution from the male and sometimes do. The question is whether it is possible for virgin eggs to develop in the case of humans and other mammals.

Virgin births have been claimed throughout recorded history, but not often believed. Theoretically what can happen in lower animals can occur or be made to occur in mammals. This seems to be the case. The difficulty has been that only one or at the most a few eggs are shed from any mammalian ovary at a time and such eggs, after being fertilized, develop readily only within the maternal body. The outside world is alien to them and they do not easily tolerate either direct observation under the microscope or experimentation. And in games such as these, humans, whether adult or egg, are far more intractable than are rabbits or mice. Yet, in the case of rabbits, whose eggs cannot readily be distinguished from human, the French embryologist Champy, nearly forty years ago, discovered among a group of unfertilized eggs kept alive outside the body that some of the eggs underwent divisions as though they had been fertilized.

Another pioneering investigator, Gregory Pincus of Boston, followed this up and tried out on mammalian eggs all the tricks known at the time that caused the eggs of lower animals to develop without being fertilized. Only an occasional egg ever reached a recognizable stage in embryo formation. Apparently it is one thing to cause a mammalian egg to divide but another entirely to keep it developing in a normal manner. This is not surprising when we consider the intimate chemical and tissue relationships that come to exist between a developing mammalian embryo and the maternal body. So Pincus treated unfertilized rabbit eggs as before, namely, by taking them from the tubes of the parent and keeping them for a short while in a warm saline solution, and then transplanted them into other virgin rabbits. From a large number of trials, some of these virgins gave birth to normal baby rabbits.

Clearly the egg is all-important, in mammals as in other creatures; and since man is a typical mammal in most respects the human egg alone is potentially a human being, whereas the human sperm and its bearer are a doubtfully essential prop. Yet through the ages, for reasons more connected with evolution than development, fertilization of eggs by sperm has become so ingrained a custom that the eggs of few kinds of creatures naturally develop without the awakening contact. On the whole men can take heart that their role in the scheme of things is still secure. Yet there is a small cloud on the horizon that suggests unsettling things to come, of man's own making, and of this we will speak again. At the moment we are concerned more with the process of fertilization itself, for it is in our understanding of this that our control of propagation and possibly of sex is based.

During the fertilization of an egg by a sperm, whether human or some other, three important events occur. Almost every kind of sperm has a long, thin, lashing tail that drives it forward and a roundish so-called head that contains the nucleus and has a small specialized region at the tip that fuses with the surface of the egg when contact is made. The primary event is this contact with the egg surface. Within seconds the whole of the outer layer of the egg substance becomes activated and egg development can proceed without the remainder of the sperm cell entering the egg at all. This step is called activation and is equivalent to the pricking of the frog egg with a contaminated needle. The egg is awakened and starts to develop, but any particular qualities of the male parent carried by the sperm nucleus have yet to be introduced.

Normal fertilization, however, involves much more. The sperm head itself penetrates into the interior of the egg, leaving only the now useless tail at the surface, its day being over. Sperm nucleus and egg nucleus fuse, and the nucleus of every cell of the embryo-to-be will contain a replica of the combination. All the genes carried by the chromosomes of both sperm and egg will be present in the nucleus of every body cell of the individual that subsequently develops. Such is biparental inheritance, and it is the basis of all human diversity—the spice of our lives.

Although visibly alike, there are actually two kinds of sperm, produced in equal numbers. Fertilization by one kind results in a male, by the other a female. The die is cast at conception, to be male or female, and can never be changed, although occasionally some sexual confusion may arise.

Our understanding of human and other reproductive processes is fairly recent, mostly from studies made since late in the last century. If we go back as far as the Greeks, who are given most of the credit for laying the foundations of our present advanced and turbulent civilization, we find the belief that males are generated on the left side of the womb and females on the right and that more males are born when the north winds blow and more females when the wind comes from the south. Yet it was Aristotle himself who said that he who sees things from their beginning will have their finest view of them.

From that early period until the invention of the microscope about three centuries ago, the wildest imaginings were rife and the beginnings of individual human life were wrapped in mystery and superstition. Throughout medieval times people believed that worms, flies and other crawling things were the spawn of the humid, putrid substances in which they were seen to occur, serpents grew from women's hair that had fallen into water, mice came from fermenting wheat that had been in water for three weeks—an observation possibly induced by the brew itself—and so on; and all this as recently as the time of the Pilgrim Fathers.

By the beginning of the seventeenth century men were willing to observe directly and describe things for themselves rather than continue arguing forever about what the ancient Greeks thought they knew. The new knowledge that we now are building on began with the chicken and the egg. The question was not whether the chick came from the egg, but where did the egg come from? If you clean a hen for the spit and look at what you are doing, it is obvious enough that a hen's eggs are formed in the ovary. The point is that for two thousand years those who cleaned

hens did not care, and those who might have been inter-
ested in where eggs came from only read books, and ancient
ones at that. Then at last the microscope brought new
sight, though one could hardly call it insight, for the new
enthusiasts, peering through the tube of their primitive in-
struments, now thought they saw the human face in the
head of a sperm and compressed body and limbs in the tail,
the whole structure of a human being in miniature. And
not only that, but each microscopic homunculus contained
a smaller one, one inside another, until the trail was traced
all the way back to Adam.

The hottest arguments, in science at least, usually arise
when two sides each have a hold of part of the truth and
mistake it for the whole. Egg enthusiasts among the early
microscopists considered spermatozoa to be nothing but
minute parasitic worms preying on the eggs, though admittedly derived from the male parent, and therefore any
resemblance a child might have to its father was said to be
merely the result of some prenatal influence. Sperm pro-
tagonists on the other hand were equally convinced that
the egg was just a shelter in which the little sperm could
pass its critical phase of growth, and therefore any resemblance a child might have to its mother was simply the result of maternal nourishment in the womb. Pieces of a story
rarely make enough of a tale, and now in our present enlightenment we are comfortable in our knowledge that as
a general rule the egg and the sperm intimately unite, unequal though they be, and together produce the embryo.

The mammalian reproductive system is amazingly successful. Rabbits for instance are notoriously able to pro-

pagate, as their overrunning of the Australian continent since their introduction in recent times has shown. Other mammals are not far behind in their overall capacity, and man is no exception. That single human egg descending from one or the other of the two ovaries inexorably in every woman once a month throughout a third of a century is as much a threat to the peace of the world as the earth has ever known. And in any woman the two ovaries operate as a working pair. Ordinarily one egg, or ovum, matures once a month alternately from the ovary of one side and then the other, although often one ovary will take a rest for several months while the other picks up the slack and does the monthly chore for both. In fact when one ovary is surgically removed for whatever reason and is permanently out of business, the surviving ovary takes over the complete burden with no seeming reduction in fertility. Production goes on, no matter what. Infertility in a woman may be sad or even tragic for her and her husband as individual people, but the potentiality for breeding on the part of the human race knows no bounds.

Males in their own way are even more productive, for the average human male is usually fertile to some degree as long as he lives, from the age of fifteen to ninety-five, in some instances. In his case both the quality and the numbers of the spermatozoa contained in the semen emitted at any one time are more important than the frequency of intercourse. For even when safely introduced into the female vagina the sperm must make, for them, the fantastic journey through the cervix and uterus and up the left and right tubes to meet the egg somewhere in the upper reaches of whichever side it happens to be.

Of the four to five hundred million sperm usually launched during a single orgasm, probably only about two thousand ever reach the region of a tube where fertilization must take place if it is to occur at all. And even then their work is not over, exhausted though they may be, for they have merely reached the outer wall of the citadel of the egg. Penetration of the egg is a feat indeed. In terms of their own size and condition, however, the journey of the sperm may be likened to the one-thousand-mile ascent made by salmon on their breeding migration up the Yukon River from the ocean, through rapids and falls and other hazards, to reach the quiet seclusion of the headwater streams and shed their eggs and milt, only to die of exhaustion when they have served their purpose. So with the sperm in the female tract. Of all set free at the start, none survives except the single sperm that succeeds in penetrating an egg, if egg there be awaiting it. Half a billion sperm may seem an enormous number for the accomplishment of such a small end, yet anything less than twenty million appears to be too few to be effective.

Yet fertility and sterility are problems that have plagued mankind through the centuries. For individuals and for states alike, there always seems to be too much or too little, never the happy mean. Numbers of sperm and the presence of eggs are vital but are not the whole story. For timing is crucial, even in the good circumstances when egg and sperm are in perfect condition and man and woman at their cooperative best.

The ripening egg in the ovary is nurtured within its follicle, which is a blisterlike structure that bulges from the surface of whichever ovary has an egg about to be released. The follicle ruptures and the egg escapes, is ovulated, on the thirteenth or fourteenth day before the beginning of the next menstrual period, and passes either directly into the tube awaiting it or perhaps into the abdominal cavity close by. This occurs once every month with equal regularity in the married woman and mature virgin. For sexual intercourse to result in fertilization it must take place within fory-eight hours of ovulation. Otherwise the unfertilized egg disintegrates and the next possible onset of pregnancy must wait another month. Of course if pregnancy is something to be avoided rather than courted, this critical period in the middle of the monthly menstrual cycle is a time to be avoided by any amorous couple, at least when nature is otherwise allowed to go her way. This, of course, is the basis of the rhythm method of birth control, which calls for continence during the female fertile period. Theroretically the method should work well, but human beings of both sexes and all ages are incorrigibly incapable of keeping accurate count for any length of time and are also innately optimistic and overwilling to take chances. Moreover the human male is not only unpredictably impulsive but spermatozoa may well survive for two days in the upper reaches of the tubes, waiting in ambush for any newly ovulated virgin egg to venture forth a little later. In any case, to become pregnant or not to become pregnant, man and woman need to keep their eye on the clock, although not to the exclusion of all else.

An egg is usually fertilized soon after it has left the ovary and entered the wide funnel of the tube extended to receive it. After entering the tube, left or right as the case may be, the egg sheds its nest of follicle cells and is ready to receive a sperm. Actual fertilization takes place in the upper reaches of the tube, which is as thin as the lead of a pencil, and the first stages of development occur as the egg slowly descends to the womb. It divides as it goes, once during the first day, again during the second day and only on the fourth day does the cleaving egg reach the womb where it must implant if it is to survive and continue development. By this time it has become a small ball of about sixty cells, a stage known as the blastocyst, because it contains a small central cavity. And for a while the blastocyst remains suspended in a sea of uterine milk. Eventually, ten days or so following fertilization, the blastocyst becomes imbedded in the wall of the womb, and the union between mother and embryo is established. Even then a woman will not have missed her first menstrual period and will have had no intimation of pregnancy. In fact until implantation is well and truly made, pregnancy cannot really be said to have occurred. Although accurate statistics are difficult to obtain, it appears likely that about one-third of all fertilized and developing human eggs fail to implant properly and pass on to oblivion. After normal, vigorous implantation has occurred, however, there is little on earth that will shake it loose.

One of the quieter tragedies of life is infertility when a couple desperately wants to have one or more children. Their personal need as individuals is acute, no matter how overpopulated the earth may be already, and infertility is therefore something to be overcome if possible. There are many causes, in both sexes. To begin with, in the woman ovulation, or egg production, must be normal, otherwise there is nothing to work with. The tube funnel must function properly for picking up the egg, or else the egg may become lost in the abdominal cavity. The tubes must permit open passage for sperm to ascend and for a fertilized egg to descend to the womb. And the developing egg must be able to implant itself in the lining of the uterus, or womb. Blocked tubes are a common cause, particularly following a pregnancy, and are generally readily taken care of. Failure of implantation is difficult to diagnose and more difficult to remedy and perhaps not even wise. Failure to ovulate, the primary cause of sterility of so many women throughout history, has been an intractable problem until recently. Now a cure has been found that tends to go too far the other way. The treatment employs hormones or a new experimental drug that mimic the reproductive cycle and stimulate the ovaries to ovulate, the procedure being repeated monthly until pregnancy is achieved. The risk is that a woman who has been yearning for a child for years finds herself confronted with several at once, possibly as many as five, an alarming prospect for any parent.

Infertility, or sterility, may not be the woman's fault at all. Under normal circumstances, so far as we now know, no human egg develops without having been fertilized by a sperm. Sperm, however, may be manufactured in insufficient numbers or in faulty condition. In either case fertilization fails to occur, no matter how well conditioned an egg may be. And while infertility in a woman may be overcome with truly overwhelming consequences, the treatment of male infertility and incontinence is less likely to be successful, is less spectacular when it is and is therefore a less challenging problem for medical science. It is of little concern to anyone except the man himself, unless he be a monarch, and of course to his wife.

There are several causes of male infertility, leaving aside possible psychological or dietary factors. It may have a genetic basis that may be irremedial. It may result from hormonal inadequacy, which may itself be genetic in origin. Or sperm may be imperfectly produced or perhaps not produced at all because of too high a temperature in the testes as a result of fever, too hot baths or failure of the testes to descend from the overwarm abdominal cavity into the relatively cool scrotal sacs during prenatal development. Sperm may in consequence be unable to make the journey to the head of the tubes, either because of insufficient numbers to survive the hazards or because of insufficient energy or abnormal motility. They may succeed in reaching the trysting place but be unable to react properly with the egg. Or they may even succeed in penetrating an egg but do more harm than good. To make an infertile man fertile may boost his ego, but it is playing with fire to some extent. No sperm is better than poor sperm, and the same can be said of eggs. In the end it is the quality of the offspring that matters, rather than any feeling of achievement on the part of prospective parents. Yet most married couples want children to raise, even when they cannot ordinarily produce them themselves. They may adopt infants under certain rather stringent conditions, or they may compromise in a rather new-fashioned way if it is the man who is infertile.

Artificial insemination is now widely practiced although with no publicity. It is not illegal, although legal difficulties concerning inheritance may conceivably arise at a later time. The immediate difficulty is primarily psychological. The practice is merely a procedure carried over from livestock breeding to human beings. We are all mammals, particularly in our reproductive processes, and for the most part what is feasible for one is feasible for another. Man differs only on that he himself is master and has a lot to say about what goes on—that is, speaking of man as a kind of animal and not as an individual human male who may or may not be master in his own household.

In livestock breeding generally, it has long been the practice to collect semen from pedigree bulls and rams and to ship it all over the world for the insemination of cows and ewes, a relatively very inexpensive alternative to shipping the animals themselves. The semen, with its contained high-grade sperm, is first rapidly frozen after the addition of glycerine to prevent the formation of ice crystals around the still-living cells. In fact such frozen material may be stored and still be in good condition when thawed out even years later. There is no technical reason why this cannot be done for human beings.

As things are, however, there is no present need to establish sperm banks of frozen material. If a couple can blink their eyes to a little irregularity, they are entitled, with the cooperation of their family physician, to have healthy sperm from an anonymous donor introduced artificially close to the womb of the fertile woman at the proper time. If pregnancy results, then both wife and husband have all the experiences of pregnancy and delivery, with the knowledge that the baby is genetically half theirs and is legally their own. Neither the donor nor the recipient is aware of the other's identity. Only the doctor knows, and it is his responsibility to select the best donor possible, usually from a hospital staff. The choice is of prime importance, and so is the psychological adjustment of the couple to having a child by this procedure. But the prospects of having a healthy and intelligent offspring are better than in the case of most adoptions, where the mother may be wayward and the father unknown. Some states already have a law legalizing artificial insemination and also legitimizing the offspring of such a procedure. Elsewhere the pratice may still be in a sort of limbo, neither illegal nor officially legal.

CHAPTER 3 *Not to Be*

Too many people, whether in state or family, can be embarrassing, and most societies have practiced birth control in one form or another. When need is recognized and accepted, morals and ethics accommodate, for custom leads the way. Even infanticide has been practiced with equanimity in primitive tribes and high civilizations alike; what is right or wrong varies with the times, with changing circumstances and man's understanding of them. The control of fertility has always been a major problem, for human kind at large and most other forms of life are only too fertile. Even when war, pestilence and famine continue to do their worst, the human capacity to breed has always been sufficient to recreate the population problem. The reproductive urge has been designed to take care of all emergencies and not at all with the welfare state in mind. And it is part of nature's security system to associate pleasure with the essential acts of life. Our appetites have been our collective salvation throughout the past, but now that we are somewhat too successful we desire to eat without becoming fat and to have sex without conception. So contraception and other means of limiting pregnancies are on their way to universal adoption in a world that is at last becoming forced to recognize its oneness.

Contraception means the prevention of conception, the prevention of fertilization of the egg. It is a biological engineering problem that is simple enough in its way. In its cruder forms, which are nonetheless fairly effective, the procedure consists of putting a mechanical barrier between the descending egg and the rising tide of spermatozoa, either by the use of a vaginal diaphragm or a condom sheath. The latter is the only device that not only puts the reponsibility on the male, who at least should carry his share, but also protects either partner from the possibility of venereal infection, whether gonorrheal or syphilitic. For married couples it is presumably unnecessary in this respect.

No contraceptive method is one hundred per cent effective, although we are getting remarkably close to the mark. And human beings are forgetful, and nature has a way of bypassing even the greatest obstacles. But with no contraceptive procedure at all, pregnacy usually follows pregnancy until death or menopause calls a halt. What contraceptive techniques do accomplish is to reduce the odds from a near certainty of conception year after year to very small chances indeed. An eminent obstetrician–gynecologist has pointed out that if the older methods of contraception are conscientiously employed, in spite of any curtailment of pleasure, the chance that pregnancy follows is about the same as being injured in a car accident, an unlikely event yet all too common. The newer techniques, however, reduce the chance of pregnancy following intercourse to that of being struck by lightning, something that all but the most fearful would ignore. Any child who can make it in spite of these odds deserves to be born.

Before the arrival of the pill and the loop, the only comparably effective contraceptive technique was surgical, that is, sterilization. This is not the same as castration, which means actual removal of the reproductive glands with serious consequences to the personality of the patient, and it does not affect the sexual urge or satisfaction but merely renders the act infertile. In a woman the operation may be made through a small incision in the abdomen, usually at the time of a Caesarian section and for reasons associated with the circumstances that led to Caesarian birth. It consists of tying off the two tubes and removing a small part of each tube so that eggs can no longer descend to meet with spermatozoa. Sterilization of a woman is generally permanent, for it is difficult to rectify the situation. Yet nothing has really been changed except for the prevention of passage. The monthly cycle of ovulation and menstruation continues, and the sex hormones keep breasts firm and eyes sparkling as before. Occasionally, however, such interrupted tubes have grown back together and allow sperm to reach an egg, a surprise to all concerned. The corresponding operation in the male is very much easier; all that is involved is the tying off of the thin vessel that conducts the sperm from the testes within the scrotum to the sex organ, which can be done in a few minutes under novocain in a doctor's office. It is almost literally a semipermanent

27

procedure, for if later there is a change of mind and fertility is again desired, the reverse operation is about fifty per cent successful.

The pill, which already needs no other name even though its chemistry may change, is clearly here to stay and has a potential impact upon the world of man eventually greater than atomic bombs. The oral pill, almost one hundred per cent effective if taken on schedule, can solve the contraceptive problem of almost all women.

The pill works by gently interfering with the body's own chemical hormonal control of the process of ovulation and does not even bring about the destruction of an unfertilized egg, although it does suppress its freedom to go adventuring. The only real casualties of intercourse under the rule of the pill are the millions of spermatozoa, which are restricted in any case to their one crowded hour of glorious life before exhaustion snuffs them out. No egg awaits them, and none can win the race. In other words, ovulation is suppressed. The effective agent in the pill is a combination of two female hormones similar to those the female body produces every month. The use of the pill is simplicity itself, and the monthly cost will continue to decrease. The living system on which it operates, however, is exquisitely delicate and complex. To be effective the pill must be taken daily over a period of twenty days. At the end of this time the pills are discontinued and a light menstrual period follows, five days after which the pills must be taken again for another twenty-day cycle. Better pills are continually being made, but only minor improvements are possible because the early product is itself so good.

The search for the pill has been long and fanciful. Women down through the centuries have resorted to many recipes. As early as 1500 B.C., at a time when Stonehenge was the center of a civilization and bull dancers entertained for their lives in Crete, an Egyptian writer advised using a concoction of acacia tips, bitter cucumber and dates, mixed with honey. Later, though still long ago in the first century B.C., a famous Greek medical scientist prescribed willow leaves in water (because willow was thought to have no seeds), or the leaves of barrenroot finely ground and taken in wine. The effect if any we cannot tell. The present pill results from physiological studies made throughout our present century, for the fundamental body chemistry that the pill exploits has been known since 1900.

Physiologists have known that hormones secreted by a woman's pituitary gland (situated beneath the brain) cause her ovaries to ripen and ovulation to occur each month. They also knew that if the egg becomes fertilized and attaches itself to the lining of the womb, another hormone appears that cancels out the pituitary hormone and prevents further ovulation during the nine months the fertilized egg is growing into an infant. This anti-ovulation hormone, progesterone, was identified in 1934, and efforts were made to synthesize it. At almost the same time a combination of progesterone and another so-called sex hormone, estrogen, was given for several months to a number of previously infertile women and then abruptly stopped. Many shortly thereafter became pregnant, a rebound effect of a sort.

Some twenty-five years later, a long follow-up, the pill was ready and a new era begins.

After more than ten years' extensive use no evidence of real harmfulness of any sort has appeared and long-term studies of women on the pill show only beneficial effects on general health, possibly indirectly through a lessening of anxieties and tension. Since sex hormones do seem to be involved in some kinds of cancer, there was a fear that the pill hormones might in the long run have some such disastrous side effect. However, oral contraceptives not only seem not to cause cancer but apparently prevent at least one type of cancer from developing. This is cancer of the lining of the womb, which is normally shed once a month by women who menstruate, and it is the third most common cancer in women, following cancer of the breast and cervix. In fact the oral contraceptive pill is being used as a successful hormonal treatment of early cancerous conditions of the womb lining that left alone would soon become malignant.

The oral contraceptive pill is essentially an infertility or intermittent sterility pill for the female system, rather than a method of preventing union of egg and sperm when they are already on their way to a potent meeting. It is more like persuading a marriage-age girl to stay home than interfering with a bride and an unknown groom on their separate ways to church. Not even an ordaining priest should object. Of course the wisdom of the ages, as distinct from the aged, should be looked for in all records of the past, although examined and reexamined in the light of new knowledge and new conditions. The established religions in particular are mostly of very long standing and carry a heavy burden of dogma inherited from men who were eminent authoritarians in their time but would be woefully unenlightened in this present age of rapid change. A few decades ago birth control was opposed by most religious denominations. One by one they are now modifying their positions in the wake of general practice and opinion. One state after another is legalizing dissemination of birth control information and even the mother church is in the throes of agonizing reappraisement. Opposition everywhere is mainly from the elderly, or at least those that seem elderly to the younger generations. The ultimate recognition that the laws of government eventually sanction prevailing custom and may even become positively permissive may be seen in Scandinavian countries. For in these well-advanced welfare states not only is sex education a routine part of high school education but contraceptive material is freely available to older students.

The pill is effective for virgins and nonvirgins alike, and many a prospective bride begins the routine several days before the wedding, lest she become pregnant during her honeymoon and become unable to help support her young husband in the custom he expects. The other contraceptive procedure now sweeping the world, the intrauterine device, or IUD for short, the loop, can readily be put in place mainly in women who have already borne a child. Actually the loop is a modern development of an old but dangerous method of birth control, apparently now made safe by the use of materials to which the tissues of the body do not react. The devices mostly in use are made of resilient plastic in the form of a ring or a spiral that can be compressed into a thin tube and inserted into the uterus, into the womb itself, above the cervix and below the tubes. They are cheap, especially compared with the monthly cost of pills, and once inserted generally remain in position indefinitely, although they can be removed at will if a woman prefers to become pregnant. How the loop acts is still a little in doubt. Enough is known to indicate that the loop acts on the wall of the womb in a way that disturbs the preparation for the developing egg, possibly causing the preparatory changes to be too little or perhaps too late. In any case the minute blastocyst stage fails to stop and implant and might just as well not have existed. As yet no embryo nor even the foreshadowing of an embryo has come into being. Moreover ignorance is bliss, for the blastocyst is only a little larger than the egg was to begin with, and its passage through the womb is unknown and undetectable. As an alternative to the pill and for most older women especially the loop is also here to stay.

This is the day of the alphabet, and many things are now commonly known only by one or several letters. Such is the Swedish M-pill or menstruation pill, better known by the Swedish press as the A-pill for abortion. So also is another kind of pill, the so-called morning-after pill, which can be effective for perhaps two weeks, at any time from the first awakening to the first indication that a menstrual period may be about to be missed. Its action is like that of the intra-uterine device. The loop and the M-pill both affect menstruation. Menstruation is itself a phase in the monthly cycle of preparation of the womb for reception of the developing fertilized egg and is the shedding of the lining of the womb, or uterus, with resultant bleeding that follows ovulation unless an egg implants. Then the preparation cycle begins again in readiness for a possible implantation the following month.

Hormones control the timing of the process. When an egg is released from the ovary, about midway through the monthly cycle, the capsule of cells in which it has been ripening fills up with another ovarian tissue known as the yellow body, or corpus luteum. For the next two weeks this little mass of tissue produces the hormone progesterone, responsible for the growth and maintenance of the uterine lining. If the egg does not implant in the lining, the corpus luteum ceases to produce the hormone, the uterine lining is no longer maintained and is sloughed off; that is, menstruation begins. If an egg does implant, it in turn somehow signals the corpus luteum to keep up its good work until pregnancy is well established. The M-pill acts in some way to interfere with the production of the progesterone hormone, so that the uterus fails to respond to the presence of a fertilized egg, and consequently no implantation takes place. In fact a woman may take a pill at the end of every monthly cycle during which she has had intercourse and her menstrual period will occur whether she has within her a fertilized egg or not. Again, she would never know. The M-pill or another like it may well become the most general method of birth control in the future, for it is effective for at least several weeks after the need first arises, and it shares with the morning-after pill the advantage of being a once-a-month pill rather than the twenty daily pills of the look-before-you-leap kind.

The question when does life begin, specifically distinctive human life, has undergone considerable change. As successive means of contraception have been made available and public adoption privately made, a process of rationalization is evident. The laws of many countries assume that life commences as soon as the egg and a sperm unite, which is the traditional view of the Catholic Church. Now scientists and others are saying that life truly starts only when the fertilized egg attaches itself to the wall of the womb, a week after conception. That takes care of the fertilized but still unimplanted egg. With the introduction of the M-pill, which prohibits development for more than two months, comes the statement that a life is not a life until the fetus has begun to produce hormones of its own that are essential to its continuing existence in the womb.

The changing attitude of the times may be seen in the following excerpt from the majority report of the Papal Study Commission on Birth Control, as published in the *Catholic National Reporter:*

The reason for seriously rethinking the traditional teaching on the illicit contraceptive intervention as regards each and every conjugal act is based on various things: the social change in marriage; in the family; in the position of woman; the diminution of infant mortality; advance in physiological, biological, psychological and sexological knowledge; a changed estimation of the meaning of sexuality and conjugal relations; but especially a better perception of the responsibility of man for humanizing the gifts of nature and using them to bring the life of man to greater perfection.

CHAPTER **4** *The Little*
Parasite

Human beings are natural parasites from the start. Each
generation must be nurtured by the preceding one. All are
dependents—infant and mother, youth and parents, hus-
bands and wives, adults and the welfare state. From beginning to end there is a tendency to expect somebody to take
care of oneself and, if this is not forthcoming, to demand
or seize whatever may be necessary for survival. Even na-
tions act accordingly, so far as they may be permitted. We
take what we need when and where we can without much
regard for the well-being of other people or of the planet
itself. This may be the original sin that embraces all others.
Whatever the case, it is well to recognize the trait and to
see it clearly for what it is. It is evident during the earliest
days in the womb. The cleaving egg, although a product
of the maternal body, becomes an invasive parasite within
a matter of days, and the developing fetus knows no
bounds.

Human eggs in particular and mammalian eggs in general are exceptionally difficult to observe. All are of about the same minute size and look very much alike, whether of mice or men. They all develop in the safety and darkness of the womb, and stubbornly refuse to develop under any other circumstances. And they all share a remarkable evolutionary history. Much of our information consequently comes from the study of those mammalian eggs most easily obtained, primarily those of mice and rabbits, which do produce relatively large litters, live readily in captivity and never talk back; whereas a woman rarely has more than one egg at a time, is not under control and would have a lot to say if she were professionally propositioned by developmental biologists. Therefore most of what we know is only an approximation of what goes on in a human being. So we look to our closer relatives. Standing somewhere between these other mammals and our sacred selves are the monkeys. The monkey egg and embryo and the monkey womb are very similar to the human. Altogether, therefore, much has been discovered concerning mammalian development as a whole, a good deal about the semihuman development of monkeys; and finally, piece by piece, the actual course of human development has been put together through matching the early stages occasionally recovered during operations and autopsies with those of our more humble, less articulate, and helpless brethren.

During the first week following fertilization of the egg, in humans, little more than cell division occurs. For the first three or four days the original single egg cell divides slowly to from a cluster of about three dozen cells as it drifts down the tube to the uterus. There it remains free for another two or three days in a uterine fluid well supplied with sugars and salts—the sugars to sustain its energies and the salts to maintain integrity, just as all cells and tissues in the adult body are bathed in a complex, well-balanced salt solution, as witness the saltiness of blood and tears. At the end of the first week, the cell cluster has increased to about one hundred and fifty cells, is hollow at its center and is known as the blastocyst. At this time the cell mass, somewhat more organized than before, settles on the wall of the upper part of the uterus and begins to burrow into the soft lining tissue. This is the process of implantation, also called nidation, which means "nesting."

In this association of developing egg and the womb, the maternal tissues do all they can to nurture the egg and become receptive to its implantation. On the other hand the developing egg seems determined to take care of its own needs wherever possible. Its efficiency is startling. Briefly the general situation is that the egg and in particular the blastocyst it soon becomes is as truly a parasite as anything else that goes by that name. Apparently only the uterus itself really needs preparation for unqualified reception and retention of an egg, which is perhaps not surprising since once upon a time this was just the last stop before an egg was laid.

The facts speak for themselves. Here are a few experiments, although not on humans. Fertilized guinea pig eggs removed during their passage through the ducts and placed within the outer chamber of the eye, where they can be observed through the transparent cornea with the aid of a microscope, continue to divide and develop and actually become implanted in the iris. They do just as well in the eye chamber of a male mouse as in the eye of a female guinea pig. They can implant almost anywhere in the body if given the opportunity, such as under the surface of the kidney, as long as the receiving tissue is well enough supplied with a mesh of fine blood vessels, even in certain regions of the brain, eggheads in the most literal sense.

Apart from the womb itself, however, the only chance they have for becoming implanted is either in the narrow tubes or within the abdominal cavity. The developing egg, whether guinea pig or human, implants when it reaches the blastocyst stage, wherever it happens to be. If passage down the tube is too slow, it implants in the wall of the tube instead of in the womb and continues to grow. The tubes are no thicker than a piece of fine string, and before long the growth of the embryo either causes severe pain or actually ruptures the tube, necessitating an operation. Under the circumstances there is no continuation of development because the mechanics of maintenance cannot be established.

Yet there is another possibility, which is extremely rare in humans but not infrequent in rabbits and other prolific creatures. The first hazard that faces an egg on escaping from its ovary is to pass into the funnel of the oviduct. Usually the wide funnel is so placed that the egg cannot miss it, but occasionally the funnel is out of place at the crucial moment and the eggs are virtually lost within the abdominal cavity. If sperm have not already reached the upper ends of the ducts at this time, no harm is done, and the eggs die just as if they had entered the ducts but had failed to become fertilized. Sperm, however, normally ascend the tubes, and some at least escape through the funnels. Consequently eggs may sometimes be fertilized even when they have been unable to enter the ducts. In this event they will implant happily enough in the mesenteries of the abdomen or perhaps the lining of the body wall itself and continue to develop in an otherwise normal manner. The penalty is that when they are ready for birth there is no way out. They die, and then in the sterile conditions of their surroundings very slowly become resorbed. Rabbits have been opened in which a partially absorbed litter of full-term infants have been found in the abdominal cavity, together with another litter developing normally in the uterus. The force of new life is surely something to contend with. It is remarkable enough in a mouse, stupendous in a human being and almost beyond belief in the blue whale, which begins as usual smaller than a pinhead and is born in less than a year as a twenty-foot-long, two-ton mass of flesh.

In all cases the crucial event, so far as survival is concerned, is the penetration of the maternal tissue, normally that of the womb, by the blastocyst cell cluster. If it succeeds in burrowing into the wall of the womb, the chances are that it will continue its development to full term. If it fails in its initial attempt to invade the parental tissue, it fails for good. Yet at this stage it is already chemically specialized for carrying out its first project. By means of enzymes the blastocyst actively excavates a space below the surface of the womb lining, and in so doing the surrounding tissue is broken down into a nutritive broth of blood

39

and broken cells from which the blastocyst draws what it needs for further growth. The invasion process also sends chemical signals to the ovaries, by way of the maternal blood circulation, to ensure that the yellow body occupying the place where the egg used to be continues its good work of maintaining the womb tissue in its pregnancy-ready state. It is as though the embryo, if we can call it that, calls out to its mother that it is home and needs to be sustained in the manner it expects.

In all of this, where is the individual? The answer is that the individual is yet to come. At the time of implantation, even though the fertilized egg may already have become a mass of several hundred cells, not only is no one there but the decision of how many to be is still somewhat uncertain. Experiments show this, although as before they are made on small laboratory animals and the conclusions extended to the human with reasonable certainty. Thus the blastocyst of a mouse can be divided into several parts by a skillful experimenter, and each part can develop into a complete embryo. And conversely as many as sixteen mouse blastocysts have been fused together to give rise to a single mouse. Interference with the blastocyst or implanting stage in humans in certain forms of birth control is regarded by some as equivalent to abortion, yet it is hard to define what has been aborted when the very basis of an individual is absent.

Whatever we call this stage in human development, it is only potentially a human being, in fact little more so than an unfertilized human egg is a potential being. The potential is there in both cases, but the actuality is unrealized. The egg, however, is now no longer an egg, yet neither has it become an embryo. If we call it a system, then we can say that the system has more urgent things to do at this particular time than to lay out the blueprint of a human embryo. Shelter and supply lines come first. Shortcuts are taken at every turn.

Implantation is normally well under way by the end of the first week after fertilization, before a woman has had time to miss her first menstrual period. She will have had no symptoms whatever of being pregnant. Yet unless preventive measures have previously been taken, the little parasite will be completely buried in the uterine wall. It is still so small as to be barely visible even if it were not out of sight. And out of such small beginnings have come beggars and kings.

At the beginning of the second week, however, while the blastocyst has been expanding, a patch of cells on one side of the cluster becomes set apart. And during this second week, still on a microscopic scale, a rudimentary water jacket, the protective amnion, splits off from this small group of cells on one side, and what looks like a small yolk sac forms on the other. The remaining layer of the original mass of cells will produce the embryo-to-be. Only toward the end of the second week does this patch of cells begin to stretch along one axis more than the other and to have what one might call a head and a tail end and a right and a left side. This is the so-called embryonic shield.

So far, so good. The embryonic shield, from which an embryo will form, is now established and is well protected both by its location in the wall of the womb and by the amniotic water jacket, the future fetal membranes. And it is still well enough nourished by the small blood bath in which it lies. What is left to be done before the whole mechanism of support and sustenance is complete is the making of the placenta. This is the relatively large organ, finally to be called the afterbirth, that takes care of all of the nutritional and other chemical needs of the growing embryo throughout the remaining time spent in the womb, in fact until birth do them part. It is produced by the embryonic system, not by the mother, and it sustains the life of the child-to-come at the expense of the maternal body.

The beginnings of this all-important placenta are difficult to follow, difficult even to illustrate and perhaps are not really necessary for our understanding of the main event. Briefly, the outermost layer of the whole embryonic mass, known as the chorion, becomes a thick membrane with numerous short branching processes extending into the maternal tissue. As growth proceeds the whole structure, containing the shield and amnion, etc., bulges out into the cavity of the womb. That part which protrudes ceases to have anything to do with drawing sustenance from the mother's tissues. On the other hand the part that remains imbedded has to carry more and more burden, because it has to sustain the increasingly rapid growth of the embryonic tissue. From this disc-shaped area at the base of the implanted mass, the branching, fingerlike processes grow progressively larger and more numerous. Steadily, as they continue to grow into the wall of the womb, they destroy the glands, the connective tissue and the blood vessels of the maternal tissue, thus excavating space for the placental vessels that will grow out from the young embryo.

The blood of the placenta and of the mother normally, however, never mix. A barrier and filter of sorts is always present, unless something is wrong. And the placenta acts aggressively toward the tissues of the mother, takes what it needs and on the whole only what it needs, and passes out to the mother's system whatever products of its own that can be considered waste. Nothing ordinarily gets through the placenta from mother to child unless it is carried in solution in the blood and so can diffuse through the walls of the fine blood vessels and the interlocking processes. Throughout the long period of pregnancy there is no other means of communication between the mother and developing offspring. There is no direct connection between their respective nervous systems and no means for the transmission of maternal experiences except insofar as stress may produce some chemical changes in the maternal blood that may diffuse across and affect the embryo directly or indirectly. As the mother's blood flows over the surface of the placental barrier, various food elements, oxygen and other substances in solution filter through the membrane into the embryonic system. In reverse, carbon dioxide and other waste substances pass the placental barrier in the opposite direction and are eliminated in the normal way through the lungs and kidneys of the mother. When fully developed, late in pregnancy, the human placenta is a rounded, flat organ from six to eight inches across and a little more than one inch thick. Its greatest importance is during the final six months, when growth in the womb is at its greatest.

These appurtenances to the development of the person seem remote from what we feel ourselves to be, because they belong to our unconscious beginning and have been abandoned forever by the time we were born. Yet they are produced by every developing human egg and have been at one time as truly a part of each of us as were our milk teeth. These also have become forgotten except that their loss may have been to some extent disturbing or painful when we were very young. We have left part of ourselves behind, as the scar that is our navel bears mute testimony. Every human life is in a way a successive shedding of some sort of skins from beginnig to end. We carry something of the past forward into time but discard much as we go along. Simply to exist is to be in continual self-renewal, but to know this fully we also need to see ourselves from egg to eternity, whatever our individual eternity may consist of.

All the same what we regard as our self, our person, our individuality seems to be apart from all the preparatory and operational activities and mechanisms associated with development within the maternal womb, no matter how complex and wondrous they may be. The human embryo that takes shape and is finally born without the trimmings is what we are most concerned with. Where and when, in this sense, does the real person begin?

The crucial period is the third and fourth week following fertilization, when a woman first begins to wonder whether she is pregnant. Before this time an embryo cannot really be said to be present. At the end of this time an embryo is recognizable, with virtually every feature present even though the whole seems to be an elongate mass of soft jelly about one-third of an inch long. All the most important decisions and events have been made by the end of the first month. The details are yet to come, but what is already present is like a small blueprint of a massive and complex machine that is going to be made. There is a head, complete with rudimentary eyes, ears and brain, and a body with a digestive tract, heart and bloodstream, simple kidneys and a liver. And there are two pairs of small, bud-like bulges representing the future arms and legs.

By the end of the second month, often still unnoticed or ignored, the embryo has grown to about one inch in length and weighs about one-thirtieth of an ounce. It could sit on a postage stamp but is already recognizably human, with nose, lips, tongue, milk teeth buds, a rounded body and all the internal organs at work. And from here on there is more growth than development. In fact everything that will be is already present in essentials at the end of about six weeks. The embryo, as it is called up to this stage, is complete. The worst mistakes, if there are any, have been made, with the price yet to be paid. If all is well, then it most likely will continue to be well. What is left to be done is mainly the tremendous growth and further elaboration of what is already constructed, a process that continues to adulthood and is only momentairly interrupted by birth. After six weeks the embryo ceases to be called an embryo and becomes known as the fetus, in order to emphasize that another phase of existence has been reached. By the end of the second month, therefore, we can say with some assurance that the person in the womb is present, with all the basic equipment and some sensitivity, although with a long, long way to go to be fully human.

CHAPTER 5 *History in the Womb*

Beginnings are hard to pinpoint. The individual human person is present in essence by late in the second month of pregnancy but is elusive before then. And we can say that the history of the individual begins with the development of the egg following fertilization. History of a sort begins at that time, irrespective of whether the egg develops into one, two or even several persons. Yet the egg itself has had its own beginning as one of many cells produced in the maternal ovary at a time when the mother in turn was in the womb. So, generation by generation, a true continuity of substance persists, from cell to cell as cells divide. This continuity goes back, step by step and millenia by millenia, to the very beginnings of life on earth.

All existing living things are those whose thread of life extends unbroken to that dim and distant time. Yet for most of past creation the threads of life did break and more life has become extinct than has survived. We and the world about us are the lucky ones although in various degrees transformed from what we used to be. Not only the adult forms but eggs and embryos also have changed as the ages passed. This long history has in various ways impressed itself on the course of development of every mammalian egg, including the human. In fact biologists of an older generation were inclined to say that the evolutionary history of the species was actually repeated in compressed form during the life cycle of the individual. This is a statement that contains some elements of truth together with a lot of nonsense and, like any such mixture of facts and fantasy, has given rise to much controversy. Nowadays there is a tendency to deny that there is here any truth at all, which is a little like throwing the baby out with the bath water and exhibiting an empty bath.

We do start life as a single cell, for that is what the human egg consists of. And that alone seems to take us back a billion years or more to a time when all living things were solitary cells of one sort or another. These were the starting points for the evolution of all multicellular creatures, and so for the beginnings of life that led to our own existence. Primitive life evolved in water laden with salts of diverse kinds. The egg also is only able to live within the mother immersed in a salty fluid remarkably like dilute seawater, a statement equally true for almost all the cells and tissues of the body. And there is reason to see in the infinitely minute spermatozoon, with its lashing tail, that unites with the egg and stimulates it to develop, another relict of those ancient times.

Thus we begin our individual lives in the old-fashioned way as a solitary cell living and growing in a briny fluid.

And from then on until we are born and start to walk
around, we develop in a fashion that echoes the evolutionary journey that took our ancestors a thousand million
years to travel. Yet our development is far from being a
straightforward condensation of the old interminable story.
In the first place there is no time for it in the nine months
we spend within the womb. Secondly the main business of
the human egg is to develop into a human being able to
walk around and raise its voice. Every conceivable short-
cut is taken, and departures and innovations occur at every
turn. Time itself gets out of joint. Certain things that appeared fairly late in the course of our evolution show up
very early in development. After all when you build a
modern house out of old materials you use them as they
are needed, with a new plan in mind, although the old
beams and stones speak of earlier architectural forms. The
developing egg gives us tantalizing glimpses of the path
we have taken, as fish in the sea and four-footed creatures
on land. The first step, from the one-cell egg to the many-
celled state, reflects the great evolutionary advance that
opened the way to the existence of the large and complex
creatures of later times, each consisting of minute cells
present in enormous numbers. Development is character-
istically an expansion of the initial cell, the egg, by means
of multiplication; there are twelve billion cells in the human brain alone.

In observing the growth of a human embryo we are in
a way engaged in a detective story. In building the human
being, as in building the house, the old materials have become disarranged; and we do not find a fish stage or a

reptile stage in the literal sense of finding fish or reptile shapes, but we do find structures that mean "fish" and "reptile." The developing skeleton shows this clearly. The first sign of it in the human embryo is a rod of cells lying in the position of the backbone-to-be and called the notochord. This is a famous rod of tissue and was once the subject of a sermon preached in Westminster Abbey by a scientifically minded dean. It was the original and all-sufficient skeleton of our earliest swimming forebears, and in all vertebrate animals, including ourselves, it is the first trace of one to appear in the embryo. Even to this day the large lamprey eels have very little more than a relatively enormous notochord to serve as a backbone—a stiffening rod that is rigid because its cells are swollen with water, like those of a green plant stem, and not from actual hardness. In the human embryo, however, we have to look at some of the very earliest stages in order to find it, for it is recognizable only in embryos no more than a fraction of an inch long.

It is always somewhat startling to think of oneself as ever having been so minute, but the truth is that more important events take place during the time the embryo grows from about one-twentieth to one-quarter of an inch in length than in any later period. And it is only in embryos as small as this that we find the antique notochord in solitary occupation of the site of the vertebral column. Thereafter its function becomes rapidly replaced by harder and more complex materials; the series of vertebrae are laid down around the notochord first as gristly cartilage, then as harder bone. Both in evolution and in the development of the individual a line is laid out, a skeletal scaffolding built around it, at last to be replaced by a hard, resistant substance. The time when you and I were seventeen may have been critical in our adolescent romantic life, but when we were three or four weeks old, reckoning from conception, we were in a much more crucial stage. For we were more fishlike when we were a quarter-inch long than we have been at any time since. And to students of human development this is undoubtedly the most fascinating stage of all. Not only are we all there in every important way, in spite of the miniature scale, but it is almost impossible at this stage to distinguish a human embryo from that of any other mammal, whether it be an elephant or a mouse, a rabbit or a chimpanzee. They all look alike, and only slowly and gradually do the essential differences become apparent.

The reason, of course, is clear. All warm-blooded mammals are the descendants of some primitive kind of reptile, and reptiles in turn are descendants of a primitive group of fish. So it is not surprising that we all travel much the same path up to a certain point during our growth as individuals. As long as we overlook the absence of a fishy shape, we can say that the fish stage exists for a time during the early development of all land vertebrate animals. The streamlined form admittedly is missing and the embryo does not swim, although there is enough salt liquid around it to wriggle in if it were able. But everything else that makes a fish a fish is there, even in human embryos.

Look first at the outside of the month-old embryo. There is a head and neck region, a trunk and something of a tail. The trunk bears two pairs of lobelike limbs, and there is nothing to show whether they are destined to be fins or arms and legs. The sides of the neck each have several deep grooves that look exactly like those which in a fish embryo are destined to develop into gill passages. In fact the only difference lies in what happens later on, for embryonic gills they truly are. And each swelling before or behind each gill passage contains a supporting bar of cartilaginous skeleton, like the gill bars of embryonic fish. Even the heart is more fishlike than human at this stage, and it has already been beating rhythmically for a week or more. It bulges way out from the chest, and it consists of two chambers only, not the four chambers we are born with. For at first it is a simple double-action pump that forces blood through a vessel below the gill region up the sides of the neck between the gill passages to reach the great artery that runs beneath the spine. It looks like the heart of an embryonic fish, and it acts like one. Not until the human embryo is an inch in length does an internal wall transform the two-chambered heart into a four-chambered one. The wall forms slowly during the fifth to the eighth week of development, a period of about three weeks, which represents in terms of heart evolution something like one or two hundred million years.

So much for fish. Neither humans nor any other kind of mammal passes through a "fish stage" as such during its individual development. But the groundwork first laid down in the development of a fish is essentially retained as the groundwork for the development of mammal and man, like building a new cathedral upon the foundations of an old abbey. The past shows through if you know how to look for it.

The road to humanity has been a devious one, and much of the history of backboned creatures, which has been our own history, too, is the history of eggs: the shift from the sea to the rivers, when eggs changed from microscopic specks to eggs like those of frogs, which can divide without any external nourishment into more than a million cells; the shift from freshwater to the land, when eggs became relatively enormous and yolky and confined within a calcareous shell capable of developing out of water and protected from the soil; and the shift from large eggs that are laid to eggs that are retained, with consequent loss of shell and yolk. Each kind set the stage for the next. Were it not for the egg of the reptile, which is to be seen virtually unchanged in the egg of a hen, our mammalian brand of reproduction and development would never have evolved. For you cannot enclose a large, yolky egg within a rigid shell without serious consequences, no matter how necessary such a shell may be.

Fish and semiterrestrial creatures such as frogs and salamanders shed both eggs and sperm in water in the old-fashioned way. The parents have no more to do with the process of fertilization. Wrapping a shell around an egg just before it is laid, as in reptiles and birds, requires previous fertilization if the egg is to develop. Once the shell is formed it is too late. So in reptiles and in their descendants, the birds and mammals, the male must introduce sperm into the female reproductive tract in such a way and at such a time that sperm reach an egg when it enters the oviductal tube, before it descends to where the shell is added. The happy event that we know as sex comes from this ancient requirement.

Confinement of the egg had other consequences, which were coped with successfully or we wouldn't be here to talk about them. One of these was that the embryo could not grow freely from the surface of the mass of yolk. The shell formed a ceiling overhead and, in the process of sinking down in place of rising up, the embryo became enfolded by membranes that made a sort of water jacket around it. If you open a hen's egg after a week or so of incubation you can see the chick embryo within its jacket, the amnion, not only well protected in its bath but rhythmically rocked by contractions of the membranes. The other two major problems—the storing of watery waste and obtaining the all-essential oxygen—were solved as one. A sac grew out of the hinder end of the embryo and did double duty in holding waste until hatching time and in supplying a large surface rich in blood vessels, a sort of external lung. This so-called allantoic sac and the amniotic jacket were necessary for embryonic life to proceed within the shell, and the combination of them enabled the early reptiles to conquer the land.

Such was the developing egg the earliest mammals retained within the maternal body. The shell became no longer needed, a bother to make and now more of a liability than an asset. The shell-less egg continued its development safely in the lower part of the reproductive tract where the shell used to be added. Then, presumably, as nourishment to the developing embryo gradually became available directly from the surrounding maternal tissue, the need for yolk diminished and so did the yolk. Finally what had been a substantial egg, comparable to those of reptiles now living, became reduced to the microscopic proportions typical of true mammals. The essence was retained, the spark of life that may become a bat, a whale, or a man, according to the species. Shell and yolk are gone for good.

The surprising thing is that we still find the other reptilian developmental inventions in the development of all mammalian embryos, including human. Even one as small as one-eighth of an inch has a yolk sac; a water jacket, or fetal membrane; and an outgrowth corresponding to the storage sac. The yolk sac, however, is small, and it shrinks rapidly since it is empty of yolk from the start. The water jacket persists until birth. It gives the unborn fetus support and room to maneuver in, and its membrane rocks the fetus as though it were a prenatal cradle. It is the caul with which some babies are born. The yolk sac is a relict and nothing more; the water jacket remains unchanged and carrying on its original function. But the third device—the storage sac of the reptilian egg—takes over an even more important duty. It no longer stores waste material and its cavity has disappeared, but the lining of the sac remains and so does the stalk. The lining serves as the placenta that unites with the lining of the womb and transmits maternal nourishment to the embryo, and the stalk becomes the umbilical cord that joins the placenta and embryo together. The cord and the placenta, or afterbirth, are modified reptilian structures, which for a time—from about the second week after conceptioin until birth—are an actual living part of every one of us.

The things that first come to mind when we think of a mammal are hair, warm blood and milk. Even the most primitive of all living mammals, the duckbilled platypus of Australia, which still lays small shelled eggs in the old reptilian way, has these features. Its coat of hair is well formed, although its body is only halfway warm. It has no milk teats, but instead there are two long grooves from which the milk flows, extending along the abdominal surface from the chest almost to the groin. The animal itself, apart from certain special features like its snout and tail, is a living relict of a time about two hundred million years ago when the earth was still ruled by dinosaurs.

Here again we find indications of the same story in our own development. We are born naked, it is true, but during the fourth month of pregnancy a dense, fine growth of hair known as the lanugo covers the entire body of the human fetus. We lose it later on, and only a scarcely noticeable down on the face remains at the time of birth. Our nakedness seems to be newly won, for at some time in our past we were certainly covered with as good a coat of hair as any other mammal. Whether our present state is an improvement is hard to say. It would undoubtedly be more economical to grow a fur coat than to buy one.

The milk glands appear at a much earlier stage than the lanugo: when the fetus is still less than one inch long and barely two months old. Instead of growing from the beginning as a pair of glands and nipples where we expect to see them, a milk line forms extending from the armpits down each side of the body as far as the groin. It is unmistakably the primitive platypus condition, although it fails to last. The breasts develop as a pair of local growths on the line part way down the chest, while the rest of the milk line disappears. Sometimes a second smaller pair of nipples grows from the line a little farther down than the first pair, equally a relict of an earlier ancestral stage. In fact if we forget the body as a whole and follow its development structure by structure and organ by organ, we get an overwhelming sense of seeing evolution taking place before our eyes.

The developmental course of certain other organs also illuminates our more recent past. The male reproductive glands are a good example. In all backboned animals up to and including the more primitive mammals, the male testes and the female ovaries are to be found in the same location; namely, in the abdominal cavity close to the kidneys. This is the primary position for both sexes. In the two-month-old human fetus the testes are attached to the interior abdominal wall, but by the third month they have already descended into the well of the fetal pelvis, where they remain until the seventh month of fetal life. At this stage the baby could be born prematurely and have a chance to live, but its testes would still be within the body and the thin scrotal sacs would be empty. During the seventh month, however, the testes pass through the inguinal canals, which always remain weak places subject to hernia, and they reach the scrotum by the end of the eighth month. Such is the course of male development. The glands first develop in the old way, in the old place, and only slowly, as the fetus grows, do they move into their new position. It is the course of evolution repeated all over again. The descent of the testes was a gradual process in the past as well.

When a baby is born it still has some way to go before we can say that it has caught up with the times. For an infant, when it does first start to move around, progresses on all fours like a quadruped. Both hands and feet are used for walking—which is not surprising since the legs are weak—but more remarkable, they are used in the same way as by any other four-footed creatures. The right foot and left hand are placed on the ground together, then the left foot and the right hand take their place. Such is the fundamental pattern of walking on four feet. We retain it not only during our first attempts at locomotion, but we keep the pattern even walking erect. Watch yourself the next time you walk down the street. As your right foot comes down your left arm swings out, and as the left foot descends your right arm goes forward too. We are more antique than we realize. Moreover when a child at last does stand and walk on his hind feet alone, the backbone is still more or less curved in an old-fashioned arch. The final posture, which depends on an S-shaped curve in the backbone, takes several months to acquire. For learning to walk erect took place in the last phase of our evolution, the five or ten million years after we had descended from the trees. Evolutionary time and developmental time almost merge together in the end. And when we add our infancy to our prenatal life and learn to read the record properly, we see man truly as living history. It is an amazing compilation.

6 *How Many in the Womb*

Single births are customary in human beings. Yet by no means do all fertilized eggs become implanted in the womb and thereafter continue with their development, quite apart from any interference with the natural process. Whether to be or not to be remains an open question for every fertilized human egg, for much depends on the normality of the egg and sperm that made the union and also on the condition of the maternal system waiting to receive it. Conception may be the prelude to somebody, to nobody or in rarer cases may result in multiple births, which are generally newsworthy according to the number.

Multiple births are more the rule than the exception among mammalian creatures as a whole. The exceptions fall into two groups. Single births are the custom where it is advantageous to produce young as large as possible, usually so that they can run or swim soon after being born and so keep up with their traveling parents, as in horse and whale. Monkeys, apes and humans bear one at a time because the young cling to or are carried about by the mother for a comparatively very long period, and the chances for survival are greater for one than when attention is divided between two or more. Yet biologically and physiologically it is simpler to produce a litter of small helpless offspring and let the devil take the hindmost than to limit production to a single egg and embryo that may or may not be able to make the grade.

Nevertheless twins and more multiple births, actually small litters, do crop up occasionally in the course of human reproduction. The rarity increases with the size of the litter. The odds are said to be about 80 to 1 against giving birth to twins, 6400 to 1 against triplets, 512,000 against quadruplets and so on. Obviously it is a matter of chance, but chance of what? The outcome, whether twins or some larger number, is only the end result of some event occurring at a very early stage. Two or more eggs may have been simultaneously ovulated and fertilized, resulting in offspring no more and no less alike than any other group of sisters and brothers may be, apart from being all of the same age. Alternatively a single fertilized egg may give rise to two or three infants who will be virtually identical, which is a very different phenomenon. Or an egg may somehow falter tragically and give rise to something that is neither one nor two but something in between. Such is the process of twinning, whether complete or partial twins result or even more than two, as long as all come from a single egg. In the one case, therefore, we are concerned with the control system that determines whether one or more than one egg is set free from the ovary at the time of ovulation. In the other the question is how does a single developing egg manage to give rise to more than one embryo.

The controls concern both the timing and the quantity. Students of reproductive physiology have long realized that growth of the reproductive gland of either sex is controlled elsewhere in the body. The experimental work of course has been done with animals, but the system is undoubtedly essentially the same in human beings. When an ovary is grafted from one female individual to another of a different age, it becomes physiologically younger or older according to the age of the recipient. In humans, too, if one ovary is removed, the ovary of the other side quickly grows to about twice its original size, so that the original total amount of ovarian tissue is restored. A controlling agent must be present, presumably of a chemical nature and circulating in the blood, and therefore of the kind known as hormones. At least part of the control lies in the pituitary gland, the pea-size mass of hormone-producing tissue that lies just beneath the base of the brain. Ovaries cease to function in animals from which the gland has been removed, but grafts or extracts of the gland will then bring about rapid growth of the ovary in the operated animal.

Setting a process in motion is by no means the same as controlling the action. A child alone in a car may set it rolling but is incapable of stopping it. So with the pituitary hormones. They are the driving force. But in triggering ovulation and thereby stimulating growth of the yellow body in place of the liberated egg, a reaction is initiated. The yellow body hormone, progesterone, which we have already seen to be needed for the preparation of the womb for reception of a fertilized egg, circulates throughout the body. Every tissue is exposed to it. When it reaches the pituitary gland it acts as a brake. The pituitary fires the ovary by means of hormones, and the ovary in turn slows the action down. Between accelerator and brake the control works well.

It is not surprising, therefore, that introduction of additional pituitary or ovarian hormones into such a complex and sensitive mechanism throws the system out of balance. If the timing is upset, ovulation may fail to occur or may be out of season, with consequent prevention of pregnancy. If too much pituitary hormone is present, ovulation may be excessive, and several eggs may be liberated instead of one. Occasionally this happens naturally, with resulting fraternal twins or some larger number of nonidentical individuals. As the number increases the chances of survival become sharply reduced.

Twins usually are well enough taken care of in the womb. Quadruplets rarely all survive. The Dionne quintuplets were the first known quintuplets to live to normal infancy, let alone live to maturity, and could not have done so without the remarkable efforts made on their behalf. The Mexican mother who bore living octuplets not long ago, with previous hormone treatment, did so against odds of one in twenty trillion. Four girls and four boys were born, each weighing about ten ounces and measuring only seven and one-half inches. Actually they were well developed for their age but were three to four months premature, and all died within twenty-four hours.

The human womb is simply not equipped to bear litters, no matter how healthily normal the fertilized eggs may be. There are limits to the mechanical and physiological load the womb can sustain, and even twins and triplets may be out of luck. The hazards are the same whether the excessive ovulation has been natural or has been artificially induced by injection of the so-called fertility hormone.

Multiple births, however, are not necessarily the result of multiple ovulation. More than one embryo may form from a single fertilized egg. The term *twins* is in fact ambiguous, since it is employed for two very different phenomena. To make the distinction, the term *fraternal twins* is applied to cases where two or more individuals develop from two or more separately fertilized eggs, with all the potential differences the members of any one family may exhibit. Identical twins are those that develop from a single egg. In this case we are dealing with a twinning phenomenon that is essentially the same whether the number produced is two, three, or more, and the offspring are generally indistinguishable to a casual observer.

In North America about two-thirds of all so-called twins are fraternal, almost exactly so for whites and somewhat higher for Negroes. In contrast the majority of Chinese and Japanese twins are identical. And apart from such differences in proportion of one kind of twin to the other there are racial differences in the production of twins relative to the total population. In European countries and in North America the expectation is about eight cases per thousand pregnancies. In Japan it is less than three per thousand. In Africa generally it is about twelve per thousand, although in Nigeria it is as high as forty per thousand. These differences in type and likelihood of twins, varying as they do with the geographical distribution of the races, probably reflect true hereditary, genetical differences among them. Further analysis, however, indicates that the type differences mainly concern the frequency of fraternal twins, and identical twins occur everywhere with a frequency of between three and four per thousand births.

Fraternal twins are thus relatively common, at least in European and African races (together with their American descendants), because of a tendency for both ovaries to set free an egg at the time of ovulation. It seems more understandable that both ovaries should do so than to understand how the two manage to take turns to respond to the monthly hormonal stimulus that undoubtedly reaches both of them. For both to respond at the same time appears to be a much more minor physiological misdemeanor than for one of them to set free two or more eggs at once and the other not to liberate any. If this is so, then how do we account for triplets?

Studies of triplets show that out of every ten occasions there are six in which two eggs are involved, one of which gives rise to identical twins and the other to a single individual; there are three in which all come from one egg, that is, are identical triplets; and there is one instance in which the three individuals come from three separate eggs, that is, are fraternal triplets. In the case of the Dionne quintuplets their general characteristics and their blood constitution indicated that all five came from a single egg and that they were truly identical quintuplets.

The challenging question concerns the nature of the process that produces identical twins, triplets, quadruplets or quintuplets from a single egg. How many individuals are actually produced is less significant than the fact that more than one is produced by a single egg, for the process appears to be essentially the same in all. This is where the main interest lies, since fraternal twins are notable only in having developed in the womb at the same time. True twinning, whatever the number produced, raises fundamental questions concerning the process of mammalian development, including the vital question when does the individual as such come into being in the course of such development.

Embryologists have been producing twins experimentally in lower animals since late in the nineteenth century. Eggs that are most readily obtained or most easily worked on have been mostly used, simply for expedience, such as those of starfish and salamanders. After fertilization, such eggs follow the almost universal rule of dividing into two cells, then into four, and so on. Some of the earliest experiments consisted of separating the first two cells from one another either by mechanical or by chemical means. If not separated, each cell would give rise to a half embryo joined to the other half. When separated from one another, each develops into a whole embryo differing from the normal only in being smaller. In fact most kinds of very small eggs can be made to give rise to identical twins if the first two cells formed by division of the egg are separated from one another. This has been done with the eggs of mammals, particularly of mice and rabbits, in spite of the difficulty of obtaining such eggs and the small number obtained. There

The Person in the Womb

is little doubt that the same would hold in the case of the human egg if the experiments could be made.

If separation of the first two cells usually results in twins in place of what would have been a single individual, is this the way in which twins in the higher animals, including humans, normally arise?

If by chance the first two cells of a dividing human egg do become accidentally separated during passage down the tube, identical twins would almost certainly result. Yet all the evidence points to a very different and much later process of twinning during the development of any mammal, human or otherwise. In most such cases, ourselves included, the difficulty is that we cannot foresee that twins are going to be formed. We know only long after the actual event has taken place, and we cannot turn time backward to see how it happened.

One clue comes from a comparison of identical with fraternal twins in the womb. Fraternal twins are entirely separate from start to finish. They merely crowd each other and may be an excessive burden to the mother. They not only are separate as fertilized eggs and later as fetuses each with its own water jacket, but each has its own cord and placenta entirely distinct from the other's. If identical twins arise through complete separation of the initial two cells of the egg, each would be equally independent in having its own personal placenta. Yet in all cases observed, identical twins share their placenta, and so do identical triplets and quadruplets. There is one placenta for all, even though each is encased in its own amniotic jacket, immersed in its own amniotic fluid. All this strongly suggests that the single egg implants in the usual way in the wall of the womb at the blastocyst stage, *before* the real process of twinning begins.

Fortunately for investigators of the twinning process there is one mammal that can be relied upon. This is the nine-banded armadillo, which delivers identical quadruplets and never anything else. As a mammal it is of course not at all closely related to our own kind, yet a mammal is a mammal, and reproductively and developmentally speaking we are all fundamentaly the same. What happens reguarly in this species of armadillo, whereby four identical offspring are produced during the development of a single egg, is almost certainly essentially the same process that occurs occasionally in human development and results in two or more identical offspring. To see what happens we have to start with an early stage of development, when the single placenta is being formed and only a germ disc foreshadows the subsequent appearance of an embryo. The all-important event concerns what happens in that embryonic disc.

In the case of all single births, whether of mouse or man, the first sign of an embryo-to-be is a streak of dense tissue that forms along the long axis of the shield-shaped disc. Everything follows from that. In the armadillo the disc is round, and instead of a single so-called primitive streak developing, four streaks appear, one in each quarter of the disc and arranged somewhat as the spokes of a wheel. Each of these gives rise to an embryo, and each develops its own amniotic envelope. Yet all are part of the original blastocyst and disc, and all share in the production of the single placenta. Since a placenta is always truly a part of a developing individual, the quadruplets are truly united in their common placenta until birth finally separates them. In humans, therefore, the twinning process is something that occurs after implantation in the uterine wall is already complete. In any case one definite conclusion can be drawn; namely, there is no person in the womb even in a rudimentary state until the developing egg has been well implanted, since the developmental decision whether to be one or more than one person is yet to be made.

What determines whether one or more than one embryo shall form during the critical disc stage is another question. All developing mammalian eggs at this stage are inaccessible and experimental investigations so far are impossible. Such insight as we have comes from experiments with the developing eggs of trout and chick, which are not retained in the body of the mother. In both of these tthe embryo develops first as a dense streak of tissue, along the axis of a round or a shield-shaped disc, very much as in a mammal, although on a larger scale. In either case if the developing egg is chilled for a short period just before the primitive embryonic streak is due to appear and is then warmed up again, some degree of twinning is most likely to occur.

Whatever normally goes on is clearly a very subtle business, which is easily disturbed. The effect of cooling and warming may be likened to stopping a group of racing athletes when one was about to take the lead and then letting them start up again. The chances are that the individual who was about to lead fails to get a good start and two or three others take the new lead at the same moment. There may even be collisions and imperfect performance, and this is true for both athletes and embryos under stop-and-go circumstances such as these. However this may be, there is little doubt that the simultaneous appearnce of two, three or four rudiments on an embryonic disc is one means by which twins, triplets or quadruplets are produced.

However, twins can result from a complete or a partial splitting of the tissues growing under the influence of the primitive streak or the embryonic disc. The primitive streak is normally responsible for laying down, so to speak, a single entire embryo. This is a very complex process. On rare occasions it may lay down two complete embryos, which will be identical twins. Unfortunately imperfectly duplicated embryos may be formed. Most of these are monsters that are dead on birth, although the two-headed calf that used to be seen occasionally at a circus showed that live birth and survival are not impossible. When duplication is almost but not quite complete, the process results in Siamese twins.

Accidents of this sort are as likely to occur during human development as in any other. In earlier times there was little chance of being born alive and small chance that the mother herself would live through childbirth. Now, by means of Caesarian section, practically anything can be extracted from the womb without risking the mortal hazard of natural passage. Imperfect, or Siamese twinning, may appear as a pair of almost complete individuals joined together chest to chest or rump to rump by little more than flesh. Surgery can then separate them. More often the union goes deeper, and vital organs such as the liver may be shared between them. Many have been born that have lived long lives in their conjoined state. Sometimes the union, to call it that, is much more extensive or more awkwardly placed. And on one ocasion at least, a two-headed baby, which is essentially the same duplication phenomena exhibited to a lesser extent, has been removed at term from its mother and kept alive for a time. And as medical technology continues to improve, triumphs of this sort are likely to become more common. The moral or ethical questions involved in so doing are another matter. Technical proficiency and wisdom are not related.

Twins raise many questions, leaving aside the fraternal twins, which are not truly twins at all except for the timing of their development and birth. The so-called identical twins and the various types of partial twinning, whether called Siamese or not, present the whole problem of personal identity in its most challenging form. Even when we restrict ourselves to well-made, separate, apparently identical twins, the question of who is who evokes a dusty answer.

CHAPTER 7 *Male and Female*

Nature demands diversity. Such is the essence of life. And, apart from identical twins and other cases of multiple products from single eggs, no two individuals are ever exactly the same. This is a fundamental part of the scheme of things. Individually we not only look different and behave differently from one another but the differences extend down to the finest details of our body chemistry.

The greatest difference between human beings, however, is so obvious we tend to take it for granted. This is the difference between the sexes. When for instance we speak of a brother and sister looking alike we are emphasizing the relatively minor characteristics that have nothing to do with sex and we are ignoring the sharply distinguishing sexual features. Differences in eye color are trivial beside maleness and femaleness. Yet essentially the same hereditary mechanism is involved in each.

Sex is both primary and secondary. Primarily it is the distinction between those individuals that have egg-producing ovaries and those that have sperm-producing testes. In addition to this fundamental difference there are all those secondary characteristics that make an individual physically, emotionally and psychologically either masculine or feminine. Some of these secondary characteristics are more directly concerned with the reproductive process than are others, for example, the penis and the temperature-controlling scrotal sacs and sperm-storage structures in the male, and the clitoris, vagina and uterus in the female. These relate to the mating process proper. Less directly related but yet significant are those features publicly proclaimed to some degree in even the most prudish society, namely, the flat-chested hairiness, the deep raucous voice and the relatively heavy musculature and aggressiveness of the fully developed male, and the seductive curvaceousness and more sweet-toned voice and personality of the female. When to all of this we add all the differences in metabolism and behavior patterns we see two types of human beings so unlike one another that it is a wonder that they can coexist at all, particularly in such intimate proximity. Since the sexes do get along together so remarkably, it should be possible for different races and nationalities to do so as well.

The die for sex is cast at conception. In man the question whether to be male or female is irrevocably determined as soon as the egg and the sperm unite, even though it may still be open whether an egg will produce a singlet or twins. Both the egg and the sperm contain twenty-three distinctive chromosomes, of which one is a so-called sex chromosome. The fertilized egg therefore contains forty-six chromosomes, two of each kind, one pair being sex chromosomes. All the body cells of the individual-to-be will possess an identical set of these chromosome pairs. The two members of each pair of chromosomes are essentially alike in twenty-two out of the twenty-three pairs. In the remaining pair, the sex chromosomes, they may be alike or may be very unlike. This is the chromosomal basis for sex determination. If there are two female or X-chromosomes, the constitution of the individual will be female. If there is one X-chromosome together with a relatively small male or Y-chromosome, the individual will be male.

Only the body cells of an individual have the double set of chromosomes. When the time comes to produce reproductive cells, male or female as the case may be, the total number of chromosomes is halved, and each mature egg and mature sperm contains a complete set of chromosomes but only one of each kind. In the case of egg cells, therefore, each will contain a single X-chromosome because there were two X-chromosomes in the cells that gave rise to them. In the male however, when the sperm cells are finally produced, half of them receive an X-chromosome and half of them a Y-chromosome, because the cells that gave rise to them contained the XY combination. Therefore all ripe eggs are alike in this respect, each having one X-chromosome. But fifty per cent of the sperm will have an X-chromosome and fifty per cent will have a Y-chromosome. It is this that determines the ratio of the sexes. Since at the time of fertilization of an egg the sperm are usually present in enormous numbers with the X and Y types equally represented, the chances are fifty–fifty that one or the other kind will reach an egg first. Fertilized

73

eggs with an XX and an XY chromosomal constitution are accordingly produced in equal numbers, and the normal one-to-one ratio of the sexes is the result. The one-to-one ratio for the two sexes in the population at large is typical of living creatures generally, although there are exceptions. In any case we will be wise not to monkey with it, however ingenious some of us may be. As things stand, repeated studies both by geneticists and statisticians show that the sex of an infant is purely a matter of chance between the two possibilities that an egg becomes fertilized either by one or the other type of spermatozoon. In tossing a coin for heads or tails, the chance is equal that it will be one or the other.

Yet even in tossing a coin, chance will result in seven straight heads and seven straight tails in every one hundred twenty-eight throws. It is the run of the luck, and so it is in families that produce a run of girls or a run of boys. Chance has done very well for a billion years. Any interference by man can only result in an imbalance of the sexes, one way or the other, with perhaps a seesawing between two extremes. What has worked for so long should be left well alone. Even in circumstances as in Russia at the end of World War II, when war casualties accounted for a shortage of nearly twenty million men and about the same number of women destined for spinsterhood in a monogamous society, nature takes care of the situation within a generation, which is no time at all.

Sex prediction as distinct from sex control is an entirely different question. Whether it is desirable is debatable, for it involves a slight risk for the child in the womb and merely satifies an idle curiosity. Most prospective parents would like to know ahead of time what sex an expected baby is going to be, but if a parent has his or her heart set on one sex or the other, the fifty per cent chance of being disappointed should not be faced until the time of birth, when a visible living being has actually arrived and demands its immediate human rights.

Human curiosity and ingenuity are the bane and blessing of our existence. Curiosity is rarely denied, and ingenuity has already raised the shadow of doom. A little matter like poking into the fetus in the womb to see whether it is going to become a propagating female or a meddling male is already a fairly common procedure. It is now possible to withdraw fluid through a fine hollow needle from the membrane sac around the fetus and from microscopic examination of various fetal cells suspended in the fluid to determine whether the fetus is male or female.

Sex, however, is never fully one thing or the other. A man has his nipples, too, as though he might be called upon to suckle his young if the trick were known. The confusion comes from the original nature of the reproductive gland of all backboned animals from fish to man. In the early development of the individual, whether of a frog or a human being, the reproductive gland when it first appears in the embryo is a combination of both male and female components. It has a central mass of potentially male tissue and a surrounding cortical layer of potentially female tissue, like a nut in its shell. If both parts develop, a combined testis–ovary would result. The individual possessing such a gland would be a true hermaphrodite, as are certain fish.

In normal development of the human embryo either the central male tissue takes over and the outer part is suppressed, or the outer female layer dominates and the male tissue is suppressed.

In a sense the struggle between the sexes begins during very early prenatal life, of part against part in a basically bisexual creature. Which way the balance is tipped depends on what sex chromosomes are present in the cells. When the cells have the XX sex chromosome combination, the female part of the reproductive gland wins out. When the combination is XY, the male part wins out. Sometimes, however, through faulty processes in the ovary or testis, eggs may have the double, XX, condition even before fertilization and sperm with an X or a Y or no sex chromosome at all. Fertilized eggs may consequently have abnormal sex chromosome constitutions such as XXX, XXY or XO, and individuals developing from these will be genetic intersexes of some sort. Those with the triple-X constitution have all the appearance of normal females, superfemales if you like, although only some will be fertile. Those with the XO combination, a much more common condition, are also feminine in body form and type of reproductive system but remain immature. Individuals with the XXY constitution, however, are outwardly males but have small testes and produce no spermatozoa. Individuals with the more abnormal and relatively rarer XXXXY and XXYY constitutions are typically mentally defective and in the latter case hard to manage. On an average about two babies in a thousand will have some sort of abnormal sex chromosome constitution. In mental institutions about ten inmates out of a thousand are abnormal in this respect. The chances of the XXX and XXY conditions appearing increase with maternal age; in other words, the older the woman the more likely her ovaries will produce somewhat abnormal eggs.

Although the sex chromosomes may be primarily responsible for the decision to be male or female their orders are apparently carried out by hormones that force growth to go this way or that according to their nature—and not only during prenatal development but throughout much of postnatal life as well. This is true for all backboned creatures and not just for man and the other warm-blooded mammals. Female hormone produced in the ovary makes a lady seductive, male hormone produced in the testis causes a man to strut in her presence. Male hormone injected into juveniles makes them masculine before their time, although this is not treatment accorded to humans.

Chickens, for instance, do not as a rule attempt to mate until they are five or six months old, still young enough by any standard, but two-day-old male chicks that receive daily injections of male hormone begin to stretch and attempt to crow on the fourth day of their existence with all the gusto of a rooster. At the end of a week they begin to fight and to flap their wings. A day or two later they show the deep red wattel of the mature cock and try to mate with female chicks. The male hormone drives the growing creature toward premature sexual maturity in both structure and action.

There is little doubt that too much male hormone introduced into the male human fetus would have most disturbing consequences. In fact the stage is set for confusion to be compounded. For surprisingly enough the ovaries produce male as well as female sex hormones, while testes manufacture not only male but female as well. In each case of course more of one than the other will be produced, and it is the preponderance of one or the other that makes male and female what they are. The bearded ladies of the circus are females who failed to get the mixture right.

The effect of sex hormones on the developing person depends on the time at which they act. A young embryo may be vastly influenced, but an older individual may remain anatomically unaffected. Most of the experiments have of course been conducted on other mammals than man, particularly on pregnant rats. If the dose is heavy enough some of the hormone will pass the placental barriers and reach the embryos within the womb. Female embryos, with ovaries already present, when exposed to male hormone will be born without nipples but with the male copulatory organ. Male embryos exposed to female hormone become anatomically female although still fundamentally male—their testes are still testes although they do not descend into the scrotal sacs. These are of course abnormal circumstances. Embryos as a rule are safe from such hormonal interference. They do not manufacture sex hormones in any quantity themselves until their anatomical nature is already firmly established. Yet the knowledge gained from such experiments helps us to understand another situation, namely, apparent change of sex in human beings.

One of the most curious things about sex hormones is that the sex glands are not the only tissues that produce them. Tremendous amounts of female sex hormone are manufactured in the placenta of both male and female fetuses, not only in rats and mice but in humans as well, together with some male hormone. Usually these hormones are produced too late to do any harm, but this is not always the case.

The danger exists chiefly for the male. A female embryo is not harmed by exposure to excessive female hormone. A girl may be more feminine than usual at an early age and everyone is pleased. But the same excess of female hormone may seriously upset the masculine development. Boy babies may be born who are truly male but under the impact of the feminizing hormone look superficially female —and are reared as such. Roughly one young person in a thousand is in this predicament, as males unknowingly masquerading as women. Yet they have the muscular strength of men and on two occasions have won women's competitions at Olympic games. Now entrants have to undergo a physical examination before the events.

Individuals so mixed up are unfortunate, to say the least. And their misfortune can be of more than one sort. Most of the boys in petticoats have more or less sterile, undescended testes, an imperfectly developed organ, well-developed breasts, an unbroken voice and no beard. The female hormone of the placenta caught them at an early stage in the womb, with resulting confusion. The other kind, which is less common but is more likely to get into the news, are those cases of girls changing into men, when voice, breasts and sexual interest take on the pattern of the male, usually in late adolescence. The placental hormone had its say but not so precociously. It is cut off at birth in any case, and slowly thereafter the male hormones of the truly male individual swing the body system as far back to normal as may be possible. Whatever the outcome the situation is disconcerting, for minds can be feminized by society and not only by hormones. Correction of a mistake usually leaves the mark of erasure.

CHAPTER 8 *Lottery in the Womb*

Two questions confront us concerning the person in the womb. Who is there and what is there? Identical twins bring both questions to the fore. In most cases they are so much alike it becomes a common difficulty to say who is who. But they will, for instance, be identical male twins or identical female twins, so that we can at least say what they are in this respect. In fact whatever their hereditary peculiarities may be, whether of body type, mental capacities, hair color, eye color, sex or any other, they will be the same. However, genetic identity does not necessarily mean complete similarity, since circumstances in the womb may favor one developing fetus more than the other, or one may be somewhat smaller than the other at its inception. Moreover one twin may be a mirror image of the other in certain ways. Also, during postnatal life, the potentials for growth and fulfillment may be differently encouraged, both nutritionally and culturally, when twins are brought up separately under different conditions.

The question of *what* a person may be can be objectively answered. The question, who is who, is more difficult. Its subjective nature is brought home by a saying attributed to Mark Twain: "My twin and I got mixed up in the bathtub when we were two weeks old, and one of us drowned but we didn't know which. Some think it was Bill and some think it was me." There lies the whole problem—the identity of the individual as seen by someone else and the self-identity as felt by whoever is inside. Twins may be indistinguishable to an outsider, but each is as much aware of himself as a self-conscious person aware of the world around him as he would be if he had no twin. The same must be true for Siamese twins, in spite of the partial sharing of the body and body functions, although the sharing of virtually all experiences may have some impact. To another person they would be two, each with an independent mind and voice. One could become blind and not the other, and one could die before the other, though not by more than minutes or hours. And if a two-headed baby were ever born and kept alive, an event already shown to be possible even in humans, we would inevitably treat them as two persons even though their body was one.

There is no doubt that what we regard as the person is the mind within, flooded as it is by the universe pouring through the senses. This is what each of us is aware of being and what we implicitly feel another to be. By the same token those unforunate beings who are quadriplegics, who have survived an accident but with a broken neck and paralysis of all but the essential body functions, are still the beloved persons who see and hear and speak, who think and feel and smile and weep. No one has left, and the person remains, for worse if not for better. When does the person first come into being?

We can fend off this question by asking other questions, the kind of questions best thought about at night instead of counting sheep. For instance if the egg that gave rise to you had given rise to twins, which was a possibility, would you yourself have come into existence? Would you be one of the twins or not here at all? Two persons would exist who would be exactly what you would have been, so far as anyone else is concerned, but that is not at all the same as being alive yourself. How is it that you are the person within your skull, looking out through those particular eyes? This is the sort of puzzle that has intrigued men throughout the ages. Aristotle, like most thinkers of his time, thought that the human spirit, the person, entered the body of the fetus through the mother's navel shortly before birth, although during the seventh month of pregnancy in the case of unusually intelligent beings. Our question, however, may be one of the sort the philosopher Alfred North Whitehead had in mind when he said there are certain kinds of questions our peculiarly anthropoid type of brain is not designed to answer. Yet we can continue to play the game a little longer. If you yourself are the inevitable product of a particular egg, what difference would it have made if that egg had been fertilized by another sperm, such as one that was a determinant for the opposite sex? The answer is that you would still be, but your sex and some other characteristics would be different. But if some other egg had been ovulated and fertilized, even by the same sperm, someone else would have developed in place of you.

About all we can truly say is that the die is cast for the making of a particular person when the first unitary streak of nervous system appears on the embryonic disc, soon after implantation in the uterine wall and long after conception. From then on whoever is to be will continue to develop by a kind of self-creative process that will continue in some degree throughout the whole of life. While still in the womb the creative process—for all development is creative—is mainly the building of the living organization, with active tissues and functioning organs. The brain and its senses are the last to be ready. Certain qualities of the person-to-be become apparent long before birth, as indicated for instance by the frequency of movement and vigor of kicking, and reaction to such stimuli as loud sound or being poked. Yet in a truer sense no person is really there until the awakening at birth. Only a potentiality exists at least until half a year, more or less, has been spent in the womb.

Even so, and to change the metaphor, the cards have been dealt. All that heredity can do was determined in the beginning. All the hereditary genes for every cell were there when the egg became fertilized. And although the forty-six chromosomes present in the nucleus of human cells collectively contain two sets of essentially the same vast assembly of genes, whereby we all develop as human beings, the collections differ in minor ways, so that as individuals we are all different. No two ripe eggs have exactly the same set of genes, nor do any two sperm. When egg and sperm unite, the distinctiveness of the combined assembly of genes is therefore greatly increased. Accordingly we each have a pair of eyes of a certain design but not eyes that see quite the same as someone else's, and we each have brains and bodies resembling all other normal human brains and bodies, yet differing from them in every detail. When all differences between any two persons are added up it is no wonder that we find it so difficult to project ourself into someone else's mind or shoes. We experience different worlds and behave according to our individuality.

The differences are total. No two beings are exactly alike in their body chemistry, nor in the cells, tissues and organs that incorporate that chemistry. Racially, sexually and individually we all have our own distinctive smell, although by the same token some individuals have a keener sense for this than do others. And only rarely can tissue from the body of one person be permanently grafted to the body of another. The virtually bloodless cornea is the exception that proves the rule. If you need to replace a patch of skin for so-called cosmetic reasons, it must come from some other region of your own body unless you happen to have an identical twin available as a willing donor. It is a fact that no man can live in another man's skin. This is as it should be. The strength, durability, flexibility and hope of the human species and its capacity for change have their roots in this almost infinite variability among its members. The extent of this variability is only now becoming fully appreciated.

The old and too often repeated statement that blood will

tell does have a certain truth of its own. A blood transfusion from one person to another may be a lifesaver or may be the kiss of death, depending on the blood types. These are the O, A, B and AB groups, which represent differences based on the presence or absence in the blood of antigenic substances A and B. Group O has neither A nor B. Group A has A only and group B has B only, while AB has both. Even members of the same family differ in these respects. There are other blood differences, too, separately inherited, although one kind may be mixed without destructive effect with the blood of any other.

Every person, whoever and whatever he may be, is unique. This uniqueness lies in the genes already present in the fertilized egg. And with every step in development, the particularly individual qualities of metabolism express themselves in the growing diversity of cells and tissues and so in the total organism of the person-to-be. Every organ in the body is established during the first few weeks, and each kind develops according not only to the general inherited instructions but also according to all the metabolic and cellular peculiarities of the individual fertilized egg. This statement cannot be emphasized too strongly. We are all human, more or less, but all that makes each of us so preciously personal and self-identifiable is the sum total of these manifold distinctions. Every part of the machinery of the body, the chemical or hormonal basis of obviously mixed emotions, the range of the senses, the working of the mind and the nature of its individual qualities, together with the flamboyant distinction of being male or female, all vary greatly and all independently. There is no end to the possible combinations. And each prescription determines both the possibilities and limtations of growth and general performance of the person so endowed. We are all the products of our genes, although nurture and environment both in and after the womb may thwart or encourage fulfillment in various ways.

Every individual, from early prenatal existence to overripe old age, has to cope with the limitations and make the best of whatever physical organism he happens to have. Most of the statistics for the various structures and functions of human beings are averages. We commonly identify an average as being the normal. The average pulse rate, at rest, is seventy beats per minute for men and about eighty for women, yet among healthy adults the rates vary from fifty to ninety. Some hearts are smaller than others among individuals of the same body size. Blood flow varies accordingly, whether to supply muscles, aid digestion or keep the brain alert. The liver is the jack-of-all-trades in the body, but one person's liver varies from another's as much as two pairs of eyes differ. Kidneys vary in functional efficiency and durability. More than forty kinds of hormones are separately controlled and released in the body by the dozen or so glands, all of which are involved in one or more aspects of body growth, maintenance and activity. Each person has his own particular array of hormone-producing tissues, each has his own peculiarly changing blend of hormones. Brain and nervous system as a whole is never duplicated, for the greater the complexity the greater the variability. Sight, hearing, smell, taste, touch, temperature sensitivity, susceptibility to pain also vary greatly and in-

87

dependently of one another. The more we study the developing individual the more striking does the list of variables become, mostly independently inherited. In sum total the uniqueness of the person becomes overwhelming. Not only do no two paris of eyes look alike, but no two persons see alike. Different senses, different brains, different emotional controls, different bodies represent far greater distinctions among persons than do the more commonly recognized but more superficial differences that distinguish human races. Skin color is the least of qualities.

Life in the womb is hazardous from start to finish. The embryo, fetus or infant-to-be with its limited potentials for better or for worse is open to attack through the mother and to misfortune from within itself. The genes inherited in the fertilized egg from the two parents may or may not be all that they should be for perfect development even in the best conditions, while the circumstances in the womb may be far from good for even the best endowed human embryo. Only the perfect egg in the perfect setting may represent the hope and wisdom of the race.

With regard to genes the problem of picking the right parents or in being the right parents is that in the double shuffle of genes that takes place during the ripening of the reproductive cells and fertilization of an egg a defective gene in a chromosome from one parent may be masked by a normal matching gene from the other. A so-called normal gene is generally dominant over its defective mate and is able to maintain normal development. We each carry a large number of defective genes, but they are usually unsuspected unless an intensive study as been made of the family group, preferably through several generations. Genes may be dominant or recessive, however, without necessarily being beneficial or harmful in either case. If you have a gene for brown eyes and a gene for blue eyes in your genetic makeup, for instance, your eyes will be brown, because the brown eye gene is dominant and the blue eye gene recessive. Blue eyes show up only when a blue eye gene is inherited from each parent, for then no brown eye gene will be present. Accordingly two blue-eyed parents will produce blue-eyed children. Brown-eyed parents who carry a double set of brown eye genes can produce only brown-eyed children. Uncertainty arises when brown-eyed parents each carry a brown eye and a blue eye gene. Then in the shuffle, known as biparental reassortment, chance determines whether a particular offspring becomes endowed with two brown eye genes, a combination of brown and blue eye genes or a pair of blue eye genes. Only the last would have blue eyes, since no dominant brown eye gene would be present for the development of brown pigment in the iris.

Trouble threatens when a recessive defective gene is associated with metabolism or some vital structure. If the matching gene inherited from the other parent is normal then all goes well for the developing individual. Trouble arrives when the fertilized egg has received such a defective gene from both parents and so has a double dose, so to speak, with nothing to correct it. By the laws of chance this is always a relatively rare ocurrence, but in the enormous populations that now compose human society the actual numbers of such unfortunate combinations may seem very large indeed. And in small close communities where considerable inbreeding among related families takes place, the chances for double trouble increase tremendously.

What are the chances? They vary according to which gene or genes are involved, for some defective genes are much rarer than others among the poulation as a whole. Perhaps the commonest of inherited diseases is diabetes. An estimated 50 million Americans are carriers. All offspring of two diabetic parents are susceptible to the disease, and half are susceptible if one parent has the disease and the other has a mother, father or a close relative with diabetes. With one parent with diabetes and the other clear the chances are about one in five that they will have a diabetic baby. One of the commoner inherited diseases is cystic fibrosis, a tissue abnormality of the lungs that makes respiration difficult. If only one parent carries the abnormal gene, the disease does not show up in the offspring; but if by chance two such parents happen to come together, the pair of abnormal genes induce the diseased condition. And about one out of every twenty-five thousand babies born is so afflicted, a small chance admittedly, yet large enough to produce thousands of children among the North American community. Parents who have produced one infant with cystic fibrosis may, however, have other children that are normal. Yet in such cases the risk is one in four that any subsequent child will have the disease. With so much at stake, that is to great a gamble.

Some forms of mental retardation, bleeding conditions and deafness also fall into the same bad risk group, and advisers generally recommend that parents with one child suffering from afflictions of this class should adopt children if they want any more. Those who ignore such advice have usually had reason to regret their decision. To a lesser degree the same holds for another group of much rarer inherited conditions, such as water-on-the-brain (hydrocephalus), open split spinal column (spina bifida) and clubfoot, where the inheritance pattern is more complicated. In these cases the chances are about one in twenty-five that if one child has been born thus handicapped so will the rest.

Such are the bad risks and the not good risks. There are others. For instance the so-called achondroplastic dwarfs, whose head and trunk are of more or less normal dimensions but whose limbs fail to grow in length; congenital night blindness; Huntington's chorea, which is a progressive degeneration of the nervous system that eventually leads to death; and anonychia, in whch some or all the fingers and toes fail to develop nails.

Any member of the twenty-three pairs of chromosomes characteristic of human cells may carry an abnormal or defective gene. When such a gene is carried by a sex chromosome, male or female, its pattern of inheritance is associated with that of sex even though unrelated to any sexual structure or function.

Hemophilia and red–green color blindness are the best known examples. In about one in ten thousand males the blood fails to clot, and even the smallest injury can be dangerous. The responsible gene is carried in the female or X-chromosome. Since the female chromosomal constitution contains a pair of X-chromosomes and a normal, dominant gene will almost certainly be present on one of them, the hemophilia disease does not show up in females. On the other hand if a male gets his single X-chromosome with the defective gene, then his matching chromosome—the Y-chromosome—has no such normal gene, and the abnormal gene is free to do its worst. This leads to a complex familial situation. Daughters do not inherit the disease but remain carriers who pass it on to their sons, who will have a precarious existence. If afflicted sons have children, their sons will be free of the disease but the daughters will be carriers. And so it goes, a sort of mathematical game for anyone inclined to play with sex chromosomes and their genes as pieces. Queen Victoria was a carrier whose daughters and granddaughters transmitted the disease throughout the royal families of Europe.

The inheritance of color blindness follows a similar pattern, consisting of alternating generations of afflicted men and carrier women. If such a color-blind man marries a normal woman, all his daughters will be carriers, since each will have his X-chromosome with its defective gene, masked by the normal gene on the X-chromosome of the mother. His sons will be normal, since they possess only his Y-chromosome, which does not carry the gene at all. But half his grandsons will be color blind, since half of them will inherit his defective X-chromosome from their mothers. It is a typical crisscross sex-linked inheritance. Now you see it, now you don't.

Taken altogether it becomes obvious that diseases or growth failures of genetic origin occur in every system of the body and are of varying severity. For obvious reasons those we know best are mostly compatible with birth and survival. The list of genetic disorders is growing constantly, and hereditary diseases at present form a large part of the practice of various medical specialists. Family doctors continually encounter rheumatic fever and mental deficiency with a genetic basis. Scientists now know that over five hundred diseases, including diabetes, blue babies, rheumatic fever and schizoprenia, are the result of inherited weaknessess in the body's chemical processes. About one in fifty babies is born with some more or less serious abnormality of genetic origin, bequeathed to it by the parents. Some of these abnormalities are correctable, others are not. For the sake of everyone concerned it is better to avoid launching a handicapped child into this savage world than to produce one and try to make the best of it. The problem, however, is complex, and few persons, laymen or professional, are competent to give advice. Any couple aware of some defect among their relatives and at all concerned about transmitting such a defect to their own children should obtain genetic counseling. There are already more than two dozen counseling centers in the United States where good advice is available. Prospective parents may be told that their fears are groundless, or they may be warned of serious risk. All too often a couple learns only through a saddening experience and even then may remain so optimistic as to try and try again. As yet the training necessary to be a genetic counselor is not part of the general experience of medical education, but the time may come when it will be a necessary part of most doctors' professional equipment. Even now the available genetic counseling is the best hope and can mean happier marriages and healthier babies for tens of thousands of parents.

Genetic mistakes, however, are far commoner than is generally realized, for nature usually takes care to erase them before they become evident. Only a relative few actually get born. If anything is basically wrong with the genetic inheritance contributed by either egg or sperm, the chances are that at some time from implantation of the developing egg to late prenatal stages the embryo or fetus will abort. Late miscarriages of course are unmistakable, but the majority of those that occur during the first three months usually pass unnoticed. At least one-third of all pregnancies terminate naturally at an early stage. Otherwise monstrosities would be born in almost every family, though not necessarily to survive. Fortunately the gross errors are practically self-eliminating. Only the marginal ones manage to get born and become a problem for their parents and themselves alike.

There is a time in the life of a woman when conception generally leads to good fortune, and there are times when fortune is inclined to hide her face. The best years for childbearing, from every point of view, are the ages from twenty-one to twenty-eight. All the hormones are at their optimum, and so are all the organs of the maternal body. This period is in fact the prime of life. From the age of seventeen to twenty-one the prospects of normal pregnancy and normal offspring are somewhat less rosy, while conceptions before the age of seventeen result in greater numbers of miscarriages, stillbirths, defectives and in maternal mortality. The physiological system of the very young mother is only too likely to be incompletely prepared for reproduction.

During the first half of the thirties, when wisdom may be greater but the body seems not quite what it used to be, there is again a rise in maternal and infant mortality rates, in miscarriages and defectives. After the middle thirties there is a sudden and dismaying jump in the production of defectives, particularly of so-called mongoloids, a condition known to the profession as Down's syndrome. This is usually a more tragic event for the parents than for the child, for the mongoloid child is typically happy if reasonably well cared for. The eyefold and flat root of the nose, which gives a somewhat mongolian look, may or may not be present, but the head is generally small, the tongue fissured and intellectual development greatly retarded, ranging from idiocy to a prospective mental age of seven years. Yet with all of this the mongoloids are usually cheerful, friendly, imitative, with good memories for music and for complex situations they may have experienced. The average life expectancy is less than ten years. About one in four hundred births in North America is mongoloid. If one mongoloid has been born to a couple, the risk that the next child will also be one is several times greater.

It has long been thought that the aging of the mother has directly or indirectly been responsible for this kind of defective development, but the discovery has now been made that the great majority of mongoloid infants have one too many chromosomes in their cells. Instead of having a pair of each of the twenty-three kinds of chromosomes, an additional number twenty-one is present, totalling forty-seven instead of the normal forty-six. This small imbalance is apparently sufficient to retard the final development of the head to some extent, with calamitous effect. The chromosomal abnormality most likely arises during a late stage in the maturation of the egg within the ovary and results either from the aging of the hormonal system of the mother or from the actual aging of the eggs, which have been present in rudimentary form in the ovary since before birth of the mother. In all of nature there is a time for everything—a time for conception, a time to be born, a time to reproduce and a time to die. Man is a child of nature whether he knows it or likes it or not, and the rhythms and seasons of life govern his individual existence from beginning to end.

CHAPTER 9 *How Safe Is the Womb?*

Humans and all other mammalian creatures develop in relative safety tucked away within the womb inside the body of the mother. The eggs that eventually reach the womb, whether to stay and develop or to pass through as the case may be, are produced by ovaries even more remote from the outside world. Egg and embryo are as immune from external harm as it is possible to be. Yet the immunity is not complete. Chemicals of many kinds circulating in the blood, some simple, some of great complexity, may pass the barriers and reach the developing individual. Radiation, from cosmic rays to X-rays, may pass through the body tissues of the mother as though they did not exist and hit targets in either ovary or embryo.

At least from the time we are born to the time we die, although only until the time we cease to breed is important, every human being is continuously exposed to cosmic rays and to the radiation from radioactive substances naturally occurring in the crust of the earth. Little harm is done to the body as a whole, but the reproductive glands of either sex are particularly affected. In New York State, for example, whereas the overall average for congenital malformations is 13.2 per 1,000 births, in areas with relatively high natural radiation the malformation rate is more than 20 per 1,000 births. In the years to come radiation from radioactive wastes from atomic energy plants, let alone from nuclear explosions in preparatory or actual warfare, will become more intense. Under these cirmustances harmful mutations may be induced in even the best families, at least in their reproductive cells. Yet natural radiation, however low, may in the long run be almost as effective, because its targets, the egg mother cells and sperm mother cells in the reproductive glands, may be targets for years on end. The effects are cumulative. Radiation may cause a detrimental mutation to occur in a reproductive cell at almost any time, and with this background radiation to be coped with, active throughout our lives and throughout the ages, we are fools to add to the hazard through actions supposedly under our own control. All radiation that reaches the reproductive cells of either sex is potentially harmful. With this to begin with, no safe level of man-made radiation can possibly exist. As individuals, as prospective parents and as members of our species, we play with atomic power at our peril, whether in war or peace.

The individual, however, can guard against two sources of potential danger. Exposure of the pelvic region of the body to X-rays can result in harmful mutations in the reproductive cells of either sex and should be avoided. Certain chemicals also are likely to produce such mutations if they enter the body circulation. Mustard gas, used as an offensive weapon during World War I, is one of these. Now we must add LSD, for in one recent investigation more than eighty per cent of users studied showed an unusually high proportion with chromosomal breaks and rearrangements, representing genetic damage. In the case of some infants whose mothers had been taking the drug while pregnant, similar abnormalities were present. Whatever circulates in the bloodstream can reach the reproductive glands as readily as any other tissue or organ. LSD users, male or female, are gambling with more lives than one. Genetic damage is only the beginning. The egg developing in the womb during the whole gestation period from conception to birth is vulnerable both to radiative and chemical attack. Exposure of the pelvic region of the maternal body to massive doses of X-rays during the first two months of pregnancy is likely to produce abortion. Such exposure may be part of some routine examination undergone before pregnancy has made itself known. If the embryo does not abort, serious injury may later become all too evident, particularly to the brain and nervous system. Yet accidents of this sort can be avoided if one of the new quick tests for pregnancy is made before exposure to any irradiation.

The greatest danger and the greatest hope for the developing embryo, assuming all is well genetically, lies in its intimate tissue relationship with the wall of the womb, namely, the placenta. No matter how good a seed may be, it needs to be properly nourished and be safe from toxic substances, whether it be grain in a field or an embryo in the womb. Much depends on the efficiency of the placenta and on the uncontaminated physiological health of the mother.

The thin wall of tissue covering the fine vessels of the placental processes allows the blood of the developing infant to come close enough to the maternal blood circulating in the wall for all vital exchanges to take place between the two systems. Oxygen, carbon dioxide, anything in solution, pass freely through the delicate membrane, but blood cells, solid particles and some others are kept apart. Even fat droplets in the maternal blood have to be broken down completely in order to pass through and have to be reassembled in the fetal blood. Altogether the placenta has a huge and complex task to maintain the rapidly growing fetus, to keep it supplied with oxygen and to get rid of its waste products.

After the first few days following conception all the growth of the developing embryo and fetus depends on substances supplied through the blood of the mother. Both the quality and quantity of the nourishment are important, especially during the later stages, when the fetus grows enormously. During this period particularly the mother is truly "eating for two," but by no means eating twice as much as before. Quality is far more important than quantity, and even when the quality is good too much can be harmful. In general diet that is best for any woman who is neither overweight nor underweight is best for a pregnant woman, namely, a well-balanced, protein- and vitamin-enriched diet that maintains the correct body weight with an extra weight allowance for pregnancy that averages no more than two pounds a month for the period as a whole.

If the mother's diet is deficient, however, particularly in vitamins, the fetus may suffer more than the mother, as in fetal rickets. Maternal diets deficient in vitamins B, C and D are found to be common in women who have had a high frequency of malformed fetuses. While in one study of two hundred and sixteen mothers and infants every still-born infant except one, every infant dying during the first few days, except one, and all premature infants were born to mothers who had inadequate diets during pregnancy. It may be a pregnant woman's prerogative to be emotional and to have special desires about food, but this must take second place to the health of her child. During pregnancy she cannot afford to make mistakes, for the penalty may be death for the infant or else some form of lifelong sentence for both of them.

The surface of the placenta is the first line of defense. Yet any barrier that permits certain substances to pass through one way or the other may sometimes yield to unusual invaders. On occasion even whole blood cells manage to pass through from one system to the other. To some extent the body of the mother and of the developing infant are at odds with one another. Primitive blood cells produced by the embryo may pass through and enter the maternal blood system, with complicating consequences to itself. As a rule, however, the invasions are in the other direction. The syphilis bacterium, for instance, readily passes from mother through the placental barrier to the embryo or fetus. If this occurs at a late stage of development, the child is usually born with signs of congenital syphilis, namely, blindness, deafness and heart defects, although the disease may not show itself until later on, as a severe disorder of the nervous system. If the infection passes the barrier at an early stage, the effect is so damaging that miscarriage usually occurs. The tuberculosis bacillus also can enter the fetus by the same route, resulting in high death rate either prenatally or during the first year after birth. Most bacteria, however, fail to pass.

Generally speaking the placental barrier is most permeable to viruses—which are much smaller than bacteria and also have special means for invading cells—and to most chemical substances, normal or foreign, that circulate in the blood. Alcohol, for example, passes freely and immediately, and the blood of the fetus will have as high a content as that of the mother. If a pregnant woman takes too many cocktails and becomes light-headed, she can be sure that the sensitive, developing brain of her infant is getting much more of a jolt.

Similarly with smoking. Whether she inhales or not, tobacco smoke enters the mother's bloodstream and soon reaches the fetus. A few puffs on a cigarette and within minutes up goes the rate of beat of the fetal heart. What else may happen to the fetus is uncertain, except that a study of thousands of pregnant women has shown that heavy smokers are twice as likely to have premature babies as are nonsmokers. All drugs apparently get through, and although the effect on embryo or fetus in any particular case may not be known, all are probably harmful to some extent. Barbiturates in heavy doses, particularly during the final, predelivery stage, can cause brain damage and even asphixiation. Even aspirin may be harmful. At least it is not certainly safe. Doctors have been warned against the prescription of several drugs commonly used for motion sickness.

Many disease-causing viruses such as those of measles, mumps, scarlet fever, chicken pox and small pox are known to pass the barrier and affect the fetus. Probably most viruses that infect the mother are able to enter the fetal blood. The most notorious is Rubella, or German measles, mainly because of its frequent epidemic occurrence. It is one of the most likely viruses to infect a pregnant woman, being encountered at almost every turn, particularly in communities where young families predominate. If exposure occurs during the first three months of pregnancy, the chances are about eight to one the unborn will develop defectively. In Germany in 1964, for instance, an epidemic resulted in perhaps twenty thousand infants born with defects and in fetal deaths of similar magnitude. Any pregnant woman who suspects she has German measles should consult her doctor at once, for the telltale rash may vanish within twenty-four hours and diagnosis may become impossible. In a child or an adult the symptoms of German measles are mild indeed, only a little fever, a passing rash and somse swollen glands. But the newborn, if infected during the critical first-three-months period, is probably blind, deaf and mentally retarded, with congenital heart disease.

In fact the Rubella virus was the first clearly defined teratogen, that is, an agent that specifically causes developmental malformations. The virus is present in the throat and the blood serum of an infected person as much as a week before the rash appears. The antibody produced by the body to combat the disease appears within a day or so of the beginning of the rash, persists for years and seems to be completely protective. Consequently a woman exposed to German measles during pregnancy has no risk of either maternal or fetal risk if she has demonstrable antibody in her blood at the time of exposure, which is something that can be checked. Immunizing shots can be taken without harm to mother or fetus, despite popular belief to the contrary. The problem is that the virus infection can occur without any apparent symptoms at all, can reach the embryo unknown and enter the cells of its organs and tissues.

The defects resulting from the Rubella virus can occur singly and in all possible combinations. Infants at birth weigh mostly less than five and a half pounds and often less than four and a half pounds. Congenital heart disease and congenital cataracts are most noticeable during the first month after birth, although in many cases the defects are not noticed during the few days the newborn usually remains in the hospital. Hearing loss and brain damage become apparent only after some months, as do other conditions such as inflammation of the liver, anemia and bone disease. The most striking feature of the infection in the fetus and newborn is its chronic nature, in contrast to the acute, though mild, nature of postnatal infections. In children and adults the virus is present for a short while only, but the virus infecting the fetus is still present at birth and for some time afterward, even though antibodies may be present in the blood.

Man is clearly a drug-taking creature. In Western society the drug industry is a major enterprise. New drugs are first widely tested on large numbers of hapless laboratory animals and then more cautiously on a number of human beings before being passed by authorities and put on the market. What has not been properly tested are the effects of drugs on development, although efforts are now belatedly being made. Drugs, unless continually taken, are eliminated from the systems of mother and fetus alike after a very short time, for they are freely diffusible. Their effect depends not only on the particular drug but on the exact stage the embryo or fetus has reached at the time the drug exerts its effect.

The most shocking instance of unexpected developmental disaster occurred a few years ago. This happened because of the widespread use of a thalidomide, a mild and supposedly safe sedative taken by pregnant women, initially in West Germany and later to a lesser extent in England, Canada and other countries. Thousands of tragically deformed babies were born before the effects of the drug became known and the use of the drug was terminated. Victims of the drug typically had short, deformed, useless arms and hands; many had no arms at all, together with other abnormalities including deformed legs and feet and various defects of the ears, digestive tract, heart and large blood vessels. Yet most of the afflicted children had normal intelligence. How the drug produces these effects is still uncertain. Subsequent tests on mice, rats and rabbits have been mainly unsuccessful in producing abnormalities similar to those seen in human infants. Massive doses in rabbits tend to bring on abortions. This brings us to the more general question of how drugs and viruses may interfere with normal development and cause derangement of the delicate and complex processes concerned.

Viruses may be said to be half alive, inasmuch as they undergo propagation even though only within some kind of truly living cell. Some invade bacteria, some invade animal cells and some only plants. Particular viruses have particular tastes for particular tissues. Polio virus invades and multiplies within the cells of the human nervous system, although those of monkeys are just as choice. Mumps virus flourishes in the cells of the parotid glands. In the fetus a virus may find a greater variety of cells to its liking and produce more widespread effects, or it may even find the fetal tissues less hospitable than in child or adult. The pattern of affiliation, in other words, is complex and not well understood.

In the case of drugs the action is more readily comprehended and can be fairly simply stated: whatever is growing or happening the fastest at the time of exposure to the drug will be affected to a greater extent than growth or events proceeding at a slower rate. Limbs, for instance, grow fastest when they have just started to form, even as two pairs of tiny hemispherical bulges on the sides of the embryo. Most drugs and other toxic agents act by depressing the growth rate of tissues and are therefore capable of partly or completely suppressing the growth of limbs if present at the right time.

Unlike the limbs, which are separately initiated at their very beginning, the pair of eyes originate as a single median patch of cells in the developing brain that shortly separates into a left and right patch representing the future left and right eyes. Toxic agents, in fact even simple chemicals such as magnesium chloride, acting on an embryo at the right stage can suppress the growth and separation of the initial optic patch of cells and consequently bring about the formation of a single eye in the middle of the forehead. This is readily brought about experimentally with fish embryos and frog tadpoles, and the so-called cyclopean, one-eyed monsters occasionally born in place of a normal human infant undoubtedly arise in a similar way. Human and other embryos must be affected at an extremely early stage for this to happen, in the human during the second week following conception.

At comparatively late stages of development certain basic growth changes have still to occur. The fusion of the right and left sides of the palate and upper lip takes place relatively very late indeed, and again any drug or other toxic agent that reduces rapid growth and tissue changes may prevent the final fusion of these structures so that cleft lip and palate persist as a defect in the newly born.

Unfortunately for many prospective human beings, the whole brain, together with sense organs in varying degree, is a rapidly growing and differentiating structure throughout the prenatal period. Therefore there is a greater chance that normal brain development and sense-organ formation will be adversely affected by some toxic agent that reaches the embryo or fetus than there is for any other unhappy event. This is in keeping with the fact that the active human brain demands and gets at least twenty-five per cent of the total oxygen taken in for the body as a whole; and that insufficient oxygen for only a few minutes causes damage beyond repair. Accordingly the greatest danger to the person in the womb, other than the one-in-three prospect of being aborted at an early stage, seems to be the possibility of being born mentally retarded in some degree. Perhaps we are all more moronic than we realize, less perfectly developed than we might have been, for the witless and the dull of wit are seldom conscious of their own condition.

CHAPTER 10 *Saving the Unborn*

Saving the unborn child from death or from some fate possibly worse than death is one of the outstanding feats of contemporary medicine, comparable to the modern miracle of vital organ transplantations in later life. Whatever we may think of the wisdom of human beings in particular and the human race in general, man is surely a technological genius. And what he is able to do he seems sure to practice.

Naturally the best way to ensure the well-being of an unborn is to start with a well-implanted healthy egg endowed with the best available genes and to maintain the best circumstances throughout prenatal life. Eggs that get off to a poor start rarely make the grade, usually abort at an early stage and cause little or no concern to the mother. Of those that do complete the course, including the process of birth itself, the chance of being perfectly normal and healthy is better than nine to one. However, many of the seven per cent who are born with noticeable birth defects of some sort might well have been normal had certain precautions been taken.

To begin with one must realize that a fetus grows at an exceedingly high rate compared with the rate of growth of the mother. Increase in weight during pregnancy should relate only to the growth of the fetus and its appurtenances. The maternal body should be kept trim, neither half-starving it to keep total weight down to previous standards nor indulging in the half-true, half-false idea that one must eat for two and unwisely acquire an additional layer of fat. Fat women have fat babies, which can become a doubled hazard during delivery. A starving woman can have an undernourished fetus developing in the womb, with consequences to the baby that are hard to rectify. The change in total weight during pregnancy should be accountable by the growth of the fetus itself, together with the weight of the growing placenta, membranes and the accumulating amniotic fluid, plus some growth of the maternal breasts. The demands of the growing fetus, however, are vigorous and must be met if the infant-to-be is to have a good start in life. It will take whatever it can from the maternal system to meet its own needs, even to the detriment of the mother, but it cannot take what is not available.

Assuming a healthy egg and good implantation in the womb, the nutrition a growing fetus receives from its mother is probably the most important factor responsible for its normal development. An adult may get along on a high carbohydrate diet, although even so it is unwise and the outcome usually not too pleasing. An alcoholic gets only energy from his drink and suffers malnutrition in essential substances, including vitamins, that may eventually kill him. The good diet for all, and especially the mother with child in the womb, is relatively rich in proteins, minerals and vitamins. These are the most essential to body maintenance and to growth. They are also the most likely to be in short supply either because of prevailing poverty or because of ignorance or mistaken self-indulgence. Such a diet, combined with general weight control, is the best guarantee for a pregnant woman that all will go well for any fetus that has had a good start.

Oversimplifying and overemphasizing the picture, we can say that although all cells and tissues in the growing fetus have much the same nutritional needs, too little vitamin D in the mother's diet can result in a stunted fetal skeleton and all the deformity that goes with it. Too little protein can result in a stunted brain that at the least is smaller than it might have been and performs accordingly. As in law, ignorance is no excuse, and every pregnant woman owes to herself and her unborn child the proper nourishment that is or ought to be available.

In saving the unborn, as in all cases where hazard exists, prevention is better than any kind of cure. So just as proper nourishment prevents the untoward effects of general or particular malnutrition, so avoidance of introducing strange chemicals into the maternal system saves the fetus from a host of possible calamities. In the case of drugs the only safe rule is—don't! None can be taken with absolute certainty that the embryo or the fetus will not be adversely affected to some degree, even though the effect is not apparent until later life and perhaps never recognized for what it is.

A common difficulty in properly following such advice is that as a rule a woman is unaware or unsure she is pregnant until two months or more of a pregnancy have already passed. Yet by that time the embryo already has a brain and a beating heart and is either off to a good start or is not. The only safe procedure for a married woman in full reproductive bloom, unless she is taking some very effective contraceptive measures, is to act as though she may be pregnant, particularly during the last two-thirds of every menstrual cycle. Testing out drugs on animals is no guarantee that they can be safely used for humans. Thalidomide, for instance, so disastrous to the unborn human, turns out to be a birth control pill for rhesus monkeys, although this means only that the drug stops the whole business rather than damaging development in progress. For the time being all should be left well alone, including nasal decongestants, antihistamines, laxatives, antinausea drugs and tranquilizers. Even aspirin and caffeine can produce abnormalities in animals. Iodides commonly used in cough medicines can produce goiters in babies prenatally. Certain antibiotics can cause prenatal jaundice or slow down the growth of bones, as can excessive amounts of vitamin K and vitamin D. All depends on the health of the mother. A good diet in the first place and avoidance of infections in order to save the unborn both from the toxic effects of an infection itself and from the effect of whatever chemicals might be taken in connection with the infection is the safest course for all concerned. Unfortunately in this overcrowded and tense society, particularly in the poorer socioeconomic sections, neither sufficient knowledge nor means are generally available.

So much for prevention. What of the rescue operations? Information must come first, and it is now possible in many respects to determine the condition of the fetus some weeks before birth. The technique for doing so was invented during the late 1950's as a means of discovering the sex of the unborn infant. Most parents would like to know ahead of time whether a boy or a girl baby is going to be born. This is little more than curiosity, of little practical concern, and the advance information hardly justifies the means to obtain it. Some risk is involved, however slight.

The technique, now of more general application, is known as amniocentesis. It consists of pushing a hollow needle through the abdominal wall of the mother, through the wall of the womb and into the amniotic sac surrounding the fetus. About one-half ounce of fluid is withdrawn from the contained amniotic fluid, in which many kinds of cells of fetal origin are to be found. The sample fluid is then spun in a centrifuge to settle out the cells suspended in it. Some will be red blood cells, but many will be from the skin, lungs and bladder of the fetus, which have been sloughed off and gurgled up or urinated into the surrounding amniotic fluid and are representative of the body cells in general of the person-to-be. Geneticists first examined such cells for the presence or absence of a minute, darkly staining blob that represents the second X-chromosome of all body cells of a female individual. If found to be present, the baby would be a girl, if absent it would be a boy.

The one great need for knowing the sex of a forthcom-

ing infant concerns hemophilia. Where there is a history
of hemophilia in the family it is important to know the sex
of the unborn infant. If a girl, she may or may not be a
carrier, but she herself will be healthy. If a boy, the likelihood is that he will be a hemophiliac, and there is trouble
ahead, both during the process of birth and thereafter. In
fact most hemophiliac infants live only a few months, and
those that survive through later years do so only in consequence of extraordinary care, for even a scratch can lead
to death from loss of blood. One of the doctors in Denmark who pioneered in the early determination of sex by
means of amniocentesis applied his information drastically.
When hemophilia was known to be present in a family
and a worried couple came to him he took advantage of
the liberal Danish abortion law and performed therapeutic
abortion when analysis showed that a boy would be born,
but permitted nature to take its course in the case of a girl.
Danish law says that an abortion may be done if the child,
owing to inherited characteristics or to disturbance or disease acquired during fetal life, may come to suffer from
mental disease or deficiency, epilepsy or severe and incur-
able abnormality or physical disease.

While hemophilia is an uncurable condition and the arg-
ument for aborting hemophiliac male fetuses may be strong,
the much commoner condition known as Rh incompatibility can be taken care of. But it must be done at birth or
preferably sooner if the infant is to live. Rh stands for
rhesus, for the Rh factor was first discovered in connection with rhesus monkeys. It refers to substances associated
with the surface of red blood cells and a number of genes,

not associated with sex chromosomes, responsible for blood incompatibilities between different individuals.

In a general way, however, we can speak of blood being either Rh-positive or Rh-negative. Eighty-five per cent of Americans and Europeans, ninety-three per cent of Negroes and ninety-nine per cent of Mongolian peoples are Rh-positive, while the remaining fifteen, seven, and one per cent respectively are Rh-negative.

Both Rh-positive and Rh-negative individuals are likely to be perfectly healthy, vigorous and long-lived. So are most of those who have had one parent positive and the other negative. The trouble comes when the two kinds of blood are mixed. If a person with Rh-negative blood receives a transfusion of Rh-positive blood, the body attempts to destroy the foreign substance by creating antibodies just as if it were combating an infection.

Although one out of every seven white women are Rh-negative, if the father is Rh-positive, the child will be Rh-positive also. So far no harm arises, and in fact there is little or no threat to the life of any firstborn child. Yet during that pregnancy and particularly during delivery, some of the Rh-positive blood of the baby leaks into the mother's bloodstream, and in consequence she produces some antibodies against the blood that is different from her own. Some time later, during her second or third pregnancy, when traces of a new invasion of fetal blood occur, the antibodies multiply rapidly, cross over into the fetal bloodstream and destroy the red blood cells of the fetus. To compensate for the progressive loss of these vital oxygen-carrying cells, the fetal heart overworks, and the fetal liver and spleen, which manufacture the fetal red blood cells, become enlarged. Unless something is done, and the sooner the better, the baby will die of congestive heart failure before or shortly after birth.

A good many years ago the discovery was made that if such babies were born alive, they could be saved by draining the baby's blood and replacing it with fresh Rh-negative blood that would not war with the antibodies. If not already dead at birth, however, many babies are already too ill to survive transfusion, and it became a practice to induce labor prematurely by as much as a month. This itself is a hazardous procedure, but is justifiable for a baby whose life expectancy after normally coming to full term is practically nil.

Only by testing the mother's blood for the presence of antibodies can any indication be obtained concerning how sick the unborn baby may be. Until about 1960, when the technique of amniocentesis became routine, thirty per cent of all affected babies died despite transfusions. With the introduction of amniotic taps, however, the death rate dropped to nine per cent.

Analysis of the amniotic fluid thus obtained shows how sick the fetus may be and even how soon it may die if left alone. If the baby is far enough along without being too sick, certainly if within a month of the normal delivery date, induced labor or Caesarian section can give it a fair chance of life following transfusion. Yet premature birth by whatever means cannot be tolerated sooner than early in the eighth month of pregnancy, when as a rule too much damage may already have been done. Consequently more and more efforts are being made to save the otherwise doomed infants while still in the womb.

One approach is actual intrauterine surgery. The uterus is partly opened as though a Caesarian operation was underway, the baby is pulled part way out and a small catheter inserted in its abdomen. Then the baby is replaced and the womb closed except for the catheter. Repeated transfusions can then be made through the catheter for weeks or months until the baby becomes far enough developed to be delivered by regular Caesarian section and has a good chance to live. A more refined technique employs amniocentesis. In one case transfusions were started during the fifth month of pregnancy when the fetus was only six inches long. The exact position of the fetal vital organs was outlined by an opaque dye that had been injected into the amniotic fluid. Then a transfusion needle was inserted through the mother's abdomen while she was under a fluoroscope so that the path of the needle into the fetal abdominal cavity could be traced. Then the Rh-negative blood was dripped in several times during the course of two months until the fetal blood was completely negative and compatible. The baby lived.

As a rule a mother's first question after delivery is "Is my baby normal?" The chances are overwhelmingly in the affirmative. Her anxiety reflects the fact that abnormality can be tragic for infant and parents alike. This is particularly true when the abnormality is mental retardation. Yet some sort of mental retardation constitutes the largest single category of childhood disease, accounting for twice as many victims of cerebal palsy, blindness and rheumatic heart disease together. Close to six million Americans are classified as mentally retarded to some degree. There are many causes, for the developing brain, being the most complex organ in the body and requiring the highest concentration of blood oxygen in order to develop and work properly, is the most vulnerable target. A large number of inherited errors of metabolism are known to cause mental retardation and can be remedied if recognized in time.

One of these metabolic conditions is PKU, which stands for phenylketonuria, a genetically acquired disease commonly associated with mental retardation. In some cases an afflicted baby grows up to be normal without treatment. Typically there is a musty body odor. Estimates are that a baby will be born alive with this disease once out of every twenty to forty thousand live births. In other words it is one of the rarer causes of mental retardation but is of unusual interest in being easily identified and readily treated if discovered in time. Discovery in time is the crux of the situation and in fact is the key to successful treatment for almost any disease. Because of this urgency for recognizing diseases of genetic origin a new venture in medical science is now under way called Genetic Alert, sponsored by the Foundation for Neuromuscular Disease and by the National Institute of Neurological Diseases and Blindness. This represents the beginning of a systematic testing of children for inheritable metabolic diseases for which there is a test, where there is a possible treatment and when the disease is common enough to justify the effort and cost of routine testing. It is a short step, already being taken, to test for the disease in the blood of the unborn child.

About four hundred babies are born with PKU each year in the United States, and because the disease must be treated within the first few weeks of life at the latest, a number of states already require that all new born babies must be tested for the disease before leaving the hospital. If found to have it, they are at once put on a special diet, in place of milk, that which eliminates the substance they cannot metabolize. Further development will then be normal. Only a few drops of blood taken from a baby's heel are required for analysis. Babies with a comparable disorder called galactosemia also require a special milk substitute if they are to escape mental retardation, cataracts and convulsions. Although PKU is admittedly a rare disease, its diagnosis and treatment have been hailed symbolically and practically as an opening wedge, a gain that can be followed by other breakthroughs that will eventually reduce the general incidence of mental retardation. A national PKU crusade became responsible for the present spreading legislation, yet the American Academy of Pediatrics has issued a formal statement of opposition to any extension of PKU legislation. Obviously if everything was as simple as has been commonly believed, no such opposition would have arisen.

There are two levels of concern. One is that the routine test for PKU, which actually is a test for the presence of a particular amino acid, phenylalanine, considered to be responsible for mental retardation when present in the blood in excessive amounts, does not necessarily by itself indicate the existence of the metabolic disorder. This uncertainty would not matter were it not that the special diet, which lacks the phenylalanine nominally present in food proteins, is by no means free of side effects. Removal of this component from the diet of normal infants mistakenly diagnosed as having PKU can bring on many of the serious consequences of malnutrition. In the case of those who truly exhibit PKU, however, the treatment may save them from complete idiocy, although one doctor has argued that PKU patients saved from idiocy may become schizophrenic later in life when taken off their diet. Any child under PKU treatment needs continuing follow-up in many ways.

Quite apart from the fate of the particular individual who has been treated prenatally or postnatally for some inborn error of metabolism there is a mounting concern over what may be happening to the population at large. Before insulin was discovered a few decades ago as a means of counteracting the sugar metabolism deficiency we know as diabetes, women with hereditary diabetes did not live to produce children. Now they do so freely, and the present population in the United States is said to contain some fifty million people with this deficiency, most of them able at some time to pass on their abnormality to another and larger generation. With PKU a similar situation is beginning to arise. Current practices indicate that patients with PKU may not have to be on treatment after childhood. At the same time there is strong reason to believe that girl babies who have been successfully treated for PKU as individuals and later become pregnant women will find themselves to be in a terrible predicament.

No matter what the genetic constitution of the person in

the womb may be, the continuous exposure of the fetus to the mother's abnormal metabolism will cause irrevocable damage to its developing nervous system. The same catastrophe can be anticipated with many other unborn errors of maternal metabolism that modify the environment of the developing young. An eminent pediatrician recently stated that these are the unavoidable legacies of success in today's program of early diagnosis and treatment of hereditary metabolic diseases and that a simple calculation shows that the next few years could yield two thousand intelligent mothers who have the PKU genetic constitution. Should they eventually marry and bear children, each one will require treatment throughout her pregnancy. What we are doinig for the individual patient may ultimately do considerable harm to the next generation and eventually even to the race. At any rate, the general prospect should cause any couple about to get married and any married couple considering having children to look at each other as prospective parents in the light of their own characteristics and their hereditary background. There are risks that may be taken and some that should not.

CHAPTER 11 *Darkness into Light*

Life in the womb is a race against time. How long can a growing fetus remain in the womb, and how large and advanced can it become? Roughly nine months is the generally allotted time. When the time does come the baby must be ready to go from the dark ocean in the womb to the light and air of a strange new world. The mother must be ready to suckle it almost as soon as it arrives. And growth within the womb must not exceed the size compatible with the passage. Not least, the placenta must keep up with the ever-increasing demands of the rapidly growing infant. Everything needs to be under control, not the conscious control of human beings but the intimate and intricate mutual instructions from nerves and hormones of infant and mother together.

One can say that a baby must be born before it becomes too big to be launched through the pelvic passage of its mother, for otherwise under natural circumstances death will be the penalty for both. Nowadays Caesarian section is a relatively safe rescue operation for the mother and at any time probably an improvement on nature so far as a baby is concerned. Alternatively one can say that birth will follow whenever the placenta begins to detach from the wall of the womb, whether to yield a full-term baby, a premature infant or some earlier stage, which may be called a miscarriage. There is clearly a precise collaboration between the rate of growth of the fetus to its normal seven to eight pounds birth weight and the capacity of the placenta to grow and maintain itself and the fetus and to maintain full interlocking attachment to the maternal uterine tissue. We might say that the normal birth weight and the nine-month gestation period are arbitrary features merely related to the physical possibilities of getting born. Certainly among our fellow mammals the range is considerable, the gestation period varying from less than three weeks in the smallest creatures to about one year in the elephant and the largest whale. In general the body weight at birth is related to the size of the mother, since the width of the birth passage varies accordingly. Yet what is astonishing in human development is that nine months are required to produce less than nine pounds. A mouse at birth is small indeed, yet a human embryo of the same age weighs but a fraction of that weight and is at a much earlier stage. At the other extreme the great blue whale, a true mammal now nearing extinction, gives birth to two-ton, twenty-foot babies after sojourn in the womb only two months longer than for humans. We grow remarkably slowly but with exceptional youth.

The embryo is complete, and the prolonged surge of

growth of the fetus begins before the end of the second month of pregnancy. By this time there is a face with eyes, ears, nose, lips, tongue and even milk teeth and distinctively human to be recognizable as such, although the embryo still weighs but one-thirtieth of an ounce and is less than one inch long. By the end of the third month it weighs a whole ounce, though at a squeeze could yet be confined within a hen's egg. This is a tremendous advance, and not only as a thirtyfold increase in weight; for now the young fetus, no longer the embryo, can kick, curl his toes and turn his feet, close his fist and move his thumb, turn his head and open and close his mouth. And from this time on he swallows considerable amounts of the amniotic fluid in which he is suspended. Early in this month the fetus moves spontaneously for the first time, though the mother remains unaware of it. With the end of the third month a milestone is reached. The movements of the fetus are no longer jerky or mechanical but become graceful, as in the newborn, and more vigorous. And the individuality begins to show. Facial expressions, for instance, because of inherited patterns of facial muscles, are already similar to those of the parents. By the end of the fourth month the baby will weigh about six ounces and will reach half the height he will have at birth. This is a great increase in actual weight, from one to six ounces in a month, but it represents a much slower rate of growth than in the previous month when weight increased from one-thirtieth of an ounce to one ounce. The rate of growth slows down progressively from the very start, although the accumulation of living substance seems to mount faster and faster. Yet it is only a seeming paradox, like saying a man can jump higher than a flea, although a flea proportionate to its size jumps many times higher than a man. What is true is that the product of growth accumulates, but the growth rate itself slows down surely but steadily, and in this sense we begin to age even long before we are born.

There are several ways the presence and nature of a young fetus may be detected. X-rays, though inadvisable, pass through soft tissues and leave no shadow but show up hard material such as bone and cartilage. A little bone is already forming in the collarbone during the sixth week of pregnancy but is still unmineralized and not until after the fourth month is there enough calcium in the developing fetal skeleton to show a skeletal shadow. And by this time a mother may expect to feel the first quickening within her body as the vigor of the fetal kicks increase. Another way involves the use of sound. High frequency sound waves bouncing off the amniotic fluid are being used to picture the tiny fetus long before its skeleton can be seen on X-ray. Even a thirty-five-day-old embryo has been detected when pregnancy tests were still negative. The principle is the same as sonar, or echolocating, now widely employed to map the ocean floor or to detect schools of fish at sea and not least by bats to locate an insect in the dark.

The amniocentic technique is also being exploited as a means of observation of the developing individual. Here the examining instrument is a little thicker than the amniocentic needle and contains hundreds of slender plastic threads that transmit illuminating light rays in and out of the womb. This is the relatively new system known as fiber optics, and it is widely employed to look round corners into small and otherwise inaccessible places. By this means it has become possible to see and photograph different parts of the fetus or placenta about one square inch at a time and so to reconstruct an overall picture of the person in the womb at various stages of its progress toward its liberation.

During the fifth month a baby weighs about a pound. Activity increases, and the mother may learn to distinguish between one knock and another, between hand and foot, head and bottom and even spells of hiccuping. Moreover the habit of sleeping and waking is already present, and every baby has its own characteristic way of sleeping, some with head on chest, some with head way back. And on waking he tosses and turns, sometimes somersaulting in the sea around him. Low sounds such as his mother's voice may startle him and cause his heart to beat faster. All this and still three more months to go before the time for passing from the dark, enclosing, watery environment to the light of day. All the essential structure is there, although you could enfold the baby in your hand and hide him from view. The main developmental work is done, for better or worse since the die has long been cast irrevocably. What is left to come is further growth and greater functional efficiency necessary for survival in the more hostile and demanding world to come. Not until the sixth month has passed is the digestive system capable of taking over its proper function nor are the lungs and breathing mechanism ready to work. In fact only late in the seventh month, when most babies weigh over two pounds, are their vital organs well enough advanced to enable them to live if born. And only then is the fetus said to be viable. After that every further week spent in the womb and every pound gained during the final two months is a step toward survival in time to come.

No incubator can compare with the womb. In the womb there is no problem of breathing, for no breathing of air is possible, and all the baby's oxygen comes through the placenta from the mother. No food need be swallowed and digested, because that also reaches the blood all ready for use. The temperature is constant and ideal. The body is practically weightless, completely supported by the amniotic fluid within the membranes. And by the ninth month most of the mother's antibodies prepared for combating the various infective diseases she has been exposed to, such as measles, mumps, chicken pox, colds and influenza, plus those acquired by vaccination against smallpox and polio-myelitis, have been transferred to the baby's system. The protective membrane of the amnion, which encloses the baby and amniotic fluid under sterile conditions while in the womb, breaks and is discarded at birth, leaving the baby exposed. But for the next half year the various disease-combating antibodies recently acquired will give the baby a fair immunity.

Premature birth will occur at any time the placenta becomes detached from its hold in the uterine wall. Fetal blood continuously flows out through the umbilical cord into the placental mass and back again through the cord to the fetal system. It is a closed circulation, and oxygen diffuses into it from the mother's blood circulation in much the same way as oxygen enters the blood through the lining of the lungs when air is being breathed in later life. At four months the blood flow through the placenta is equivalent to about twenty-five quarts a day, at nine months the flow is equivalent to three hundred quarts a day. Round and round it goes, from fetus to placenta and back again in only thirty seconds and with a great deal of force. And from this continual round, all the chemical needs of the prenatal infant are steadily supplied. Sending such a waterborne, encapsulated, automatically nourished creature out into thin air is comparable to sending a man to the moon and having him step out of his capsule to survive if possible and fend for himself, except that in the case of the baby preparations for the traumatic and otherwise fatal experience have been made well in advance.

Throughout its existence the placenta has been almost exclusively in control of events. It has been a growing, self-sustaining organ in nearly but not quite complete control of the passage of vital and of waste substances between fetal and maternal blood. It also manufactures the hormones estrogen and progesterone, the same sex hormones produced in the ovaries. These two hormones, produced by the placenta in large quantities, have much to do with the maintenance and preparation of the maternal body through all phases of the reproductive process.

The primary effect of the estrogen is to cause rapid growth of the uterine musculature, necessary for expelling the baby at the time of birth. It also causes great growth of the blood vessels in the uterine wall to meet the demands of the uterine muscle and of the rapidly growing fetus.

In addition estrogen causes enlargement of the vaginal opening and relaxation of the pelvic ligaments, providing a larger passageway for birth. The placental estrogen entering the maternal system also causes great development of the milk glands in the breasts, in preparation for suckling the newly born. Until birth is actually under way, however, everything is sort of held up, tensed for action, so to speak, and waiting to be unleashed.

The actual mechanism for birth is controlled through the opposing influences of estrogen and progesterone on the uterine muscle. The first causes it to grow, the second prevents it from becoming active. As soon as the progesterone is withdrawn, whether by actual partial detachment of the aging placenta or by a lowering productive level resulting from the aging process itself, the action starts, and the mother goes into labor. Labor involves both the expulsion of the baby as such and the final separation of the placenta from the wall of the womb. Once this separation has begun, the influence of the placental hormones is ended. Not only do the uterine muscular contractions become increasingly strong and more frequent, but a hormone of the pituitary gland is now released that causes the milk glands to begin their business of secreting milk.

Premature birth may be good or bad depending on the degree of prematurity. A baby born at seven months has literally put its life into somebody's hands and may survive with difficulty. A baby born two or three weeks prematurely and therefore somewhat undersized may have drawn a blessing on both its mother and itself, but an overdue, overweight baby may be calamitous if not anticipated. The difficulty lies in the bottleneck. Whatever room there may be in the womb, the baby, full term or not, must pass out through the pelvic opening, only four to five inches wide. For a large baby great force has to be exerted to expel it; labor can be long and painful and the baby subject to serious harm, especially the head. Fortunately the shape of the head at the time of birth is flexible, and most full-term babies are born with egg-shaped, molded heads that have been squeeezd through the narrow birth canal without injury. It is somewhat of a shock to see such a newborn child for the first time, and the overanxious father might be wise to delay his introduction for three or four days, when the distorted head will have regained its normal roundness.

After the baby has been born, usually head first, the cord and placenta, the afterbirth, follow on. Nowadays the cord is cut. But even without such help both cord and placenta shrivel fast, and the cord would break at the navel and the baby be none the worse. However this may be, the placenta, the fetus, the amnion and the cord are until this time all of one piece. The fact that the amniotic membranes rupture, the cord is cut and the placenta lost, makes no difference. Until this time they are all a part and parcel of each one of us, as truly as if they were an extra, if temporary, appendage, and we each have a navel as the lifelong mark of amputation.

Once a good developing egg has become well implanted in the womb during the second week of its existence, usually all goes well until the time of birth. But getting born will be the most hazardous experience during the whole of life. More deaths occur at or near birth than between one

week and forty years. Quite apart from the physical expulsion through the birth canal and in spite of all that a
mother or nurse appears to be doing in caring for the baby,
the newborn infant has been mainly and suddenly thrown
on its own resources under circumstances that are entirely
new. With the separation of the placenta from its attachment, all supply of oxygen and nourishment have been
abruptly cut off. Lungs, liver and kidneys are suddenly
burdened by an urgent call to duty. The onset of respiration with expansion of the lungs is the first essential; but
the circulation also must soon be altered from fetal to adult
pathways, which involves closing an opening between two
sides of the heart, or else well-oxygenated blood will not
reach the head. Light, cold, gravity and many skin sensa-
tions are all experienced for the first time. It is a time of
crises, for life itself but for the brain above all. The mortality rate is 3.5 per cent.

The greatest hazards are injury during exceptionally difficult labor, the problem of Rh-negative and Rh-positive
blood incompatibility and inadequate oxygen supply during
the interval between loss of the placental oxygen source
and being able to breathe air. The predicament is comparable to that of a scuba diver who loses his tanks when deeply
submerged and must hold his breath while swimming to the
surface.

Placental failure or premature separation too soon before
delivery may cause death directly from lack of oxygen or
indirectly by causing the unborn infant to inhale amniotic
fluid and so die of respiratory distress within forty-eight
hours of birth. Death occurs at this time when either labor

is abnormal or when the fetal tolerance for the lack of oxygen associated with normal labor becomes lethal. All such deaths are really failures in the physiological adaptations to changes in the environment at birth. The great majority of babies are born head first, as though reaching for the air, but in breech presentations, buttocks first and head last, there is an added danger from obstruction of the umbilical cord even when the placenta is still in place.

Ninety-five per cent of newborn babies take their first gasp of air within sixty second of birth. The remaining five per cent do not because of depression of the respiratory center in the brain stem during the period of oxygen lack while in passage or because of drugs given to the mother to ease the pain of labor or because of pressures on the soft skull of the baby during birth that cut off circulation of blood to the brain. The main problems concern how to prevent premature labor, the causes of which are still greatly unknown, and when necessary to rectify the position of the baby in the womb before labor begins.

From first to last, from early in the womb and throughout postnatal life, the brain is most vulnerable to any lack of oxygen, because it requires so much. Consciousness goes within minutes when the supply is cut off, and the performance of the brain is clearly impaired when oxygen reaching it is reduced. Permanent but not fatal damage can occur at critical levels. One of the great unanswered questions is how much do all of us suffer during the process of getting born. We may be duller than we know and less bright than we might have been. Yet above all is the golden rule, to be born at the right age at the right time.

CHAPTER 12 *Brave New World*

What is the world of the newborn? Who is it that enters such a world? Any observant mother, unless stupefied by misinformation that babies cannot see until they are six weeks old, knows that her baby watches her face from the day it is born. There was a time when a newborn infant's mind was thought to be a completely blank slate with everything yet to be inscribed upon it. But a baby who has most likely sucked its thumb for weeks in the seclusion of the womb, heard the rhythmical sounds of speech and music or been startled by sudden noises and has been alternately sleeping quietly and wakefully kicking around, at least has something to go on.

The less than ten pounds of humanity freshly arrived upon the scene has a brain already one-quarter the weight of the adult brain, with every brain cell present that it will ever have. Whatever is lost in the years to come will be lost for good. Eyes are three-quarters as large as they will ever be, while the middle ear is almost as large as it can get.

Psychologists have long debated whether the newborn baby sees things around it much the same way as an adult sees or whether, as William James believed, his world is at first one big, buzzing, blooming confusion. Is his ability to see the world as much a part of man's genetic endowment as the ability to breathe? For a newly hatched chick, once it has dried off, fluffed up and stood up, is able to walk over to a dish of water and take a drink, with no apparent confusion at all. Why shouldn't the newborn human be able to do as much? In some ways he can, for given the chance he will suckle at his mother's breast on the first attempt, which is no mean feat on the first day of life outside.

Yet the question of seeing is crucial. If William James was right in principle, he understated the case, for then the infant's visual world should be a chaotic, frightening flow of changing shapes, edges and sizes, forever disappearing and reappearing in continuous confusion, for this is what the retina receives and gives to the mind to make sense of. The problem for the investigator is how to get an answer from an organism as helpless as a human infant, who can make few responses of any kind.

One way is the procedure followed by students of animal behavior, who have discovered a great deal concerning perception in pigeons, fishes and even worms, using a method that employs a "reinforcing" agent to strengthen the response of the creature to a particular stimulus. A pigeon, for instance, that has had food or water witheld for some time responds strongly to any stimulus that signals food or water. Human infants must be treated more gently, and in certain investigations the reinforcement employed to increase the normal responsiveness to a visual image is merely the little game of peekaboo doting mothers and their friends often play with babies. The adult jumps out smiling and nodding and speaking in front of the baby and then quickly hides again. Babies from two weeks to four or five months find the event highly reinforcing, that is, giving pleasure, or entertaining, and will respond for as long as twenty minutes to make it reoccur. Things appear and disappear, and can practically produce cardiac arrest! It is the drama of the object reappearing. Is it gone or not gone?

With this as the basis for getting responses, psychologists have discovered that a two-month-old infant, for example, is capable of much greater discrimination of space, size and shape than the blank-slate proponents expect but falls short of the expectations of those who say that a baby sees what an adult sees. The visual world of the infant is probably overwhelming at times, but it is not the meaningless buzz it was thought to be. Even the youngest babies see distinct shapes and patterns and do make out people's faces. And although a gas pain can cause a smilelike grimace, most smiles are real.

Studies of all ages from the newborn to six months show that infants like looking at a human face or a facelike pattern more than anything else. This is the earliest stage of social responsiveness, for the young infant perceives all adult faces as potential pleasure givers. Up to six months he smiles at any face that moves toward him and only later smiles at certain faces in particular. Right from the start, however, the two sexes perceive things differently. Thus girls of all ages are more visually aware of their surroundings than are boys and seem to find it harder to isolate details and ignore their background. Boy babies hear low tones better and high tones more poorly. From the beginning male and female live in somewhat different worlds and both live in a world far different from what an adult knows.

What infants can register during the first days of life is truly astonishing. They can distinguish halftones of color, diagonals and even on the very first day can track a triangle with their eyes. Within a month they can recognize objects and tell when something has been changed. Altogether a new era of direct observation of infant behavior has begun, and mountains of new information are now being fed into computers for analysis. Much of this attention has centered on the first five days of postnatal life, when babies are still in the hospital and most readily studied.

Russian psychologists employing the "orienting reflex," the eye or hand movements by which a child shows that he can anticipate certain events, have managed to investigate responses to sound in babies only two hours after birth. Americans usually employ the more sophisticated technique of recording an infant's heartbeats as a measure of attention, as in the so-called lie detector. The heartbeat slows down momentarily when attention is given. By this means it is shown that an infant's attention is at its peak when it sees something just a little unfamiliar, neither too novel nor too repetitious. Apparently there is a pleasure in the mental act of matchinig unfamiliar things to some general scheme, and an infant smiles not only for social reasons but also because he has recognized something and has a feeling of satisfaction or accomplishment. It is a basic quality of the human mind that persists throughout life, though not uniquely human since monkey and ape enjoy it, too. In fact a baby has been described as a novelty-digesting machine that devours change and grows on new experiences.

Lack of stimulation can be calamitous. Normal children raised by deaf-mute parents lose the ability to hear well, presumably because they learn to emphasize other means of communication such as hand movements and to ignore other cues. Experiments with monkeys, whose visual equipment is essentially like that of humans, show that if they spend long periods in darkness during infancy they have great difficulty in learning to distinguish objects by sight; while babies who do not have some distinctive person, whether mother or mother substitute, who comes and goes regularly fail to develop a sense of time and place. Solitary confinement of any sort is deadly at any age. Neither does man live by bread alone, nor, when it comes to an infant, by milk from a bottle. Far more is required.

The human person from infancy onward is a complex of mind and emotion and cannot be regarded as fully human if either of these is stunted. Something soft and warm and cuddly is more vital to a baby than any amount of food. Infants in an institution who are deprived of their mothers or adequate substitutes increasingly lose interest in their surroundings, stop playing, stop hoping and even stop crying. Being fed and diapered regularly by busy nurses with no time for fondling is not enough. This progressive deterioration has been called "hospitalism," and it may be seen at the other end of life when old and more or less helpless persons are subjected to similar circumstances. In the particular foundling home under study, the developmental quotient of the babies, whose mothers were too poor to keep them but who were presumably normal, fell from an initial 131 at the age of two or three months to a mere 72 at the end of the year. Yet in a nursery attached to a women's prison, where the babies were cared for every day by mothers who were mentally retarded women, delinquent minors and psychopaths, the babies' developmental quotient rose from 97 at age two or three months to an average of 112 at four or five months and finally settled back to 100 by the end of their first year, which was the norm for their age. Being fed from a bottle and kept clean, or even being breast fed, is not enough. Infants need full-time love and care from someone, not necessarily the biological mother, or they will either perish or grow up emotionally and to some extent mentally crippled. So much is involved in early development that we are only now becoming aware of, and much remains to be understood. Not least is the infant's discovery of self.

A young baby's sense of touch and temperature is even better developed than his sight and hearing, and the comfort of being held and fondled makes it easier for him to learn the distinction between self and not-self, between Me and Not-me. Most mothers hold and play with their babies and talk to them quite naturally. It is a form of enjoyment built into the maternal system to serve a vital purpose, and in this respect humans are not alone. It is part of an ancient heritage, and a baby needs such attention right from the start.

At about two months an infant's sight and hearing become keen enough so that he knows one person from another, and he is old enough to start worrying. If a stranger picks him up, he is likely to cry, a reaction that psychologists call "stranger anxiety." He isn't sure that all the persons visiting him are warm and loving. Somewhat later the worry becomes the "separation anxiety," and from about six months to eighteen months an infant seems to be really afraid of losing his mother. If he has reason to feel that he has lost his mother, he may suffer a depression severe enough to affect him throughout his life. As a rule if babies are institutionalized for only a few months and given excellent care afterward, the bad effects can be overcome. But early deprivation lasting as long as two or three years causes irrevocable harm.

Without the normal mother-infant relationship a child becomes autistic, that is, it fails to develop a personality, to develop a sense of self that can operate in relation to real experience. But such children are in no way feebleminded. The condition has been variously called severe childhood schizophrenia, suicide of the soul and most vividly the empty fortress. For they develop bristling defenses ranging from complete muteness to time-consuming and unchangeable rituals for the most fundamental bodily functions. Whenever psychologists manage to penetrate the defenses they find extreme and explosive hatred combined with an eternally thwarted but persistent longing for something that they do not have. Only when an infant has had repeated and satisfying experiences of its own effect upon its surroundings, beginning at birth, can it develop a personality or sense of self. And it is this that the so-called autistic child has missed and in some way is acutely and terribly aware of. Such cases are tragic beyond words, for it is too late for anything to be done. For time is of the essence. The inborn time schedule for normal development after birth cannot be delayed too long. If the child does not achieve effective contact with the world around him during the critical period, it may well be too late to do so at any later period, and he is left without a sense of self. There is only a feeling of total rejection and isolation. These are extreme and unusual cases admittedly, but they point up the danger that in milder degree may be all too common.

If the development of mind and emotion is all of one piece, so is the development of mind and body. Unwittingly, orphanages of various standards and in various countries have become laboratories for the study of effects of neglect or deprivations. Normally babies learn to sit alone by the age of ten months, but infants in an orphanage in Iran became so apathetic and retarded that fewer than half of them learned to sit up by the age of two years, and at the age of four the great majority still failed to walk alone. Instead of creeping before standing and walking, these children propelled themselves forward on their hands from a sitting position, and quite efficiently. If the mind does not learn, the body fails to learn also. What also is now seen to be true is that when the body fails to learn the mind too fails to become what it might have been. Body and mind are one. This is a truth never to be forgotten.

Most remarkable discoveries are coming from studies of handicapped children, particularly the supposedly hopeless cases of mental retardation resulting from brain injury of any sort. These are children who mostly cannot walk and even may be unable to move arms and legs when first brought to the Institute for Neurological Organization. When this rehabilitation center was first established shortly after World War II no one had known of a single brain-injured child ever being made well. The early treatments were traditional, namely, braces for buckling legs, occupational therapy for crippled fingers, speech therapy for uncontrollable tongues. All failed, as they had everywhere else. This was symptomatic treatment, comparable to treating the yellow color of jaundice in the case of that disease, when it is the liver that is in trouble. If anything, the crippled children became worse. The discovery that revolutionized treatment came from the inspiration to see what was happening to those children whose parents had refused the apparently useless treatment and had taken them home and left them on the floor without any further attention. None of them had gotten any worse, and many had become somewhat better. And what had been happening was that they had been doing whatever they could do by themselves. They had the freedom to do it. Those under treatment had not.

It was slowly learned that an old folk expression was sound neurology, that a child has to creep before he can walk and crawl before he can creep. Perhaps the body could teach the brain. So a team of therapists would take a child and move this arm and leg together, this arm and leg apart, that arm and leg together, that arm and leg apart, and head right, head left, regularly for months on end except for sleep. Finally this strange method was seen to be teaching noncreepers to creep by themselves and was leading creepers to walk by themselves. Then came something even stranger. The speechless children began to talk. The better they learned to speak, the better they learned to walk. And the better they learned to walk, the better they learned to read. Not only were ten-year-olds, eight-year-olds and six-year-olds taught to read, but so were four-, three- and even two-year-olds. Similarly at the Institute for Learning Disability, hundreds of schoolchildren who were failing to learn to read by look-say, phonetics or whatever, have been made into good readers by getting them down on their knees and having them creep for ten or fifteen minutes a day for weeks. The theory is that if these children had crept properly and long enough as babies, their side-to-side eye movements, combined with the symphony of muscular coordination, would have properly prepared their brains for readiness to read. These were the children who had readily accepted the hands of adults who too soon and too readily offered to help them walk. Timing is all-important. Each phase of each step depends on the previous one having been properly and fully experienced.

If brain-damaged children can be trained to do so well, why don't so-called normal children do better? Their human potential is clearly greater. One reason why full development may be none too well developed could be that certain aspects of the care of a baby are emphasized to the detriment of others. In the cool climate of northern countries particularly, where most pale-faced people live, fresh air is given great importance. Whether the baby is put outside or cool fresh air circulates in the nursery, the infant is usually wrapped up from head to toe to keep him warm and is tucked tightly under a blanket in a basket, often with a shade outside overhead to keep off the sun and the birds and the insects. This might be fine for growing tomatoes, yet the whole point of recent discoveries is that the infant is ready from the moment it is born to do much more than grow like a vegetable and in its own limited ways is already eager to explore the new universe it finds itself inhabiting. His first business is to struggle on his belly, learning to work hands and feet against the ground. On his back there is nothing but air to beat against. You give him a rattle for his first toy, but it means about as much to him as it does to you. There are five ways to play with a rattle and so to learn. He can taste it, stare at it, stroke it, smell it and rattle it. In about ninety seconds he knows all about it. And so with most things he gets a chance to investigate. As a rule they do not amount to much, and the child discovers boredom all too soon. Idle senses and idle hands amount to an idle brain. Yet a brain learns how to be brainy only by being used.

Every creature is the produce of its past, a past extending through the ages. The human past includes several vitally important phases that are incorporated in the present—the arboreal, which put a premium on eye, hand and the coordinating brain; the later ground phase, when walking and running on two limbs became marvelously perfected; and the close human family, which was the nursery for speech. This is the common heritage for every human infant. From the very beginning we each have a special kind of brain, the eye-hand brain, which requires a total development for full performance, neither one thing nor another but all together. We have a body that must go through the old 1, 3, 2, 4 four-footed locomotory sequence before gaining a balancing upright stature. And we have a unique development of one side of the brain that relates to speech, combining sound and vocal musculature. For all of these the machinery of development must be set and maintained in motion from birth onward.

Just as there is a proper time for learning and developing the muscular activties and brain coordinations associated with moving the body, limbs and eyes, so there is for developing the mechanism for speech and the acquisition of language. In fact at the age of two or earlier every healthy child is a linguistic genius. From just hearing the sounds of conversation he learns a language with its nouns, verbs, prepositons, grammar, without knowing what it is all about, and does so with amazing skill in usage, retention and associations. Yet to learn another language a few years later may be almost an impossibility, at least without an accent.

What if hearing is impaired from birth or earlier? Deaf-mutes, mute because they were deaf from the start, are pathetically handicapped and may also be to some extent retarded. There are many possible causes, one of which is the Rubella virus of German measles, for in one of every two Rubella babies the damage includes at least a partial loss of hearing. Rubella deafness, however, does not involve nerve damage, and whatever the degree of deafness may be it will get neither worse nor better during life. If the Rubella damage does not include actual brain damage, and there are new tests that can now determine whether non-responsiveness is the fault of the ear or the brain, much can be done to aid, though not cure, the child. Early diagnosis is crucial. When hearing aids are fitted to very young children, as early as the end of the first month if possible, the results can be encouraging even for Rubella babies. Dull infants often become alert and animated, and many learn to speak almost normally. When deafness is not caused by Rubella or by inherited deficiencies, as may well be the case, three-fourths of the infants fitted with hearing aids before nine months old attain unaided hearing by the age of one. How this happens is not understood, but probably the explanation is that use of the neural pathways from ear to brain encourages their functional development. For this seems to be the general rule for full development of the brain and nervous system as a whole.

Even though all babies have the same basic neural, sensory and muscular organization that needs well-timed stimulation and duration for full development, no two babies are ever quite the same. That all men are born equal refers to human rights, not human constitutions. The best that can be done is to permit and encourage the full flowering of the person. The environment can promote the expression of the full potential, or it can thwart or warp it in various degrees and ways.

Quite apart from skills, personality traits can be recognized in an infant as young as eight months that indicate whether he will become impulsive, reflective, aggressive, introverted or extroverted. Yet in all that he is and will be in structure, mind and emotion, he is and always will be a unique person. Every human being experiences a different world from that known to any other and is truly a new individual living a new life never lived before and never to be lived again. We all have eyes but do not see the same. We all have ears but do not hear the same. We all have a body, arms and legs, hands and feet, but uniquely our own in every case.

A surprising discovery of recent times, although it shouldn't be so surprising, is the apparent enormous range in structure and function of virtually every part and system among "normal" persons. This discovery comes mainly from studies of grown people but represents conditions that are present at birth. The skeletal system, the respiratory system, the endocrine system, the nervous system and even the microscopic details of the blood show a tremendous structural variation within the so-called normal range. Normal stomachs vary about six times in size and vary as much in shape. Large intestines vary greatly in arrangement. The great aortic vessel leading from the heart may have anywhere from two to six main arteries. The aorta itself varies greatly in size. Hearts differ much in structure and power and so pump accordingly. The blood supply to the brain, so vital to thought and consciousness, is very different in different individuals. Each person breathes in a different way from every other. Each has his own distinctive pattern of sensitive spots for touch, pain, cold and warmth all over his skin. No two persons can taste and smell the same way. Some smell certain substances acutely, others the same substances not at all. And so for seeing and hearing. Every infant, child and adult senses an external world in a somewhat different way from everyone else and feels inwardly and outwardly in a way uniquely his own. Personality study is itself in its early infancy.

The diversity of human beings, which is laid down long before birth, becomes evident at birth and becomes increasingly expressed through young and later life, is our saving grace. It demands tolerance for others, is the basis for pride and wonder in the self and is the source of creativity. Yet one of the greatest needs all persons have is to experience pure being. This comes in part from the streaming in of all the aspects of the outside world through the senses, flooding the mind with light, sound, smell and the feeling of flowing air. It also comes from awareness of the body in action, as sensed from within. When these sources combine, the joy of living can be intense indeed. The child develops a sense of joy and wonder. It should not be lost.

A poet has said that youth's one need is to transcend itself. This is growth. Growth of the body and its capacity to perform. Growth in living, one experience after another, filling the stores of memory with all that pours in through the senses, all that the body feels, all the emotions that flood the mind, and not least growth in the capacity of the mind to think and to put thought into action. Above all and including all is the growth of the soul, or spirit, whatever we like to call it, which is the person, a flaming, growing essence that may last as long as life or wane before its time. Each individual life is its own creation, its own cycle of renewal, which from the nature of things must have a temporal end. Each has the chance to make a lot or a little out of his own potentiality and in his time to grow in, and sooner or later the growth must become self-directing. When the striving ceases, growth is over, and the human essence which is the spirit of youth disappears or dies, leaving old disillusion in its place. Age in all its aspects is the cessation of growth. Youth is retained by everything that grows. These are biological statements that apply to all organisms. They apply to the mind as well as to the body. And every child starts with the capacity if not the opportunity to unfold and to turn every experience of living into new growth, perhaps with joy, perhaps with pain, but nevertheless into growth. The senses of childhood are open to beauty and wonder, the heart to hope, the mind to question. Who quenches it? Probably those who have already lost it. But the growing spirit or personality can keep on growing throughout its days until at last the body is held together by nothing else. It is possible to live serenely in the midst of turmoil, to keep your true face open to all men. It is possible to fight for the life of your mind as much as your body, to know that ideals are but glimpses of truth, that truth is beauty and love is harmony and that evil comes from losing them. There is richness here if only we can give ourselves to being alive and cease struggling to disown our nature. To every one we should say: this is your time on earth, take care of your life and seek no peace outside of yourself.

CHAPTER 13 *A Limit to Life*

We pride ourselves on being human, although what is human? Someone has defined man as the missing link between ape and the truly human, which emphasizes the unfinished business of our becoming. At our best, individually and collectively, we strive to express the wonder and creativity of life but always reach for something more. Yet who is the person who strives to be, to do and to become? Whoever and whatever he is, we are dealing with the center of consciousness, imprisoned somewhere within the skull and looking through the windows of the senses. Whatever the relationship of mind and brain may be, when the brain is destroyed the mind goes, too.

The person, in all essentials, resides above the neck. A quadriplegic with a broken spinal cord may be fully there except in actions to all who know him. The tragedy is frustration, but the person lives. But when the brain is damaged or poorly developed, from accident, lack of oxygen, arterial senility, or trouble in the womb, the body may function as well as ever but no one or worse than no one is there who might have been a human being. We are clearly concerned with the human spirit, with its growth, its joy, its creativity, its strength and courage. Nothing else matters in the end. The quality of the human person, the dignity of the individual, the uniqueness of the individual, the sanctity of the spirit. These are cherished, nurtured and respected. On an overcrowded planet, therefore, must the quality of life be sacrified for the sake of numbers? Must everyone and everything be born that can be born? What are the human rights of the unborn, of the newly born and in later life of she who must do the bearing?

To begin with there are no specifically human rights. There are rights that human beings confer upon themselves but deny to other creatures and at times to segments of the human race itself. Every form of life, under certain circumstances, has the capacity to outbreed all else and cover the planet with its own particular kind of flesh until doomsday strikes it down. Man already is far along the road to this condition. There is neither room nor support for all that we can produce. Even the elephant, the slowest breeder of all, could trample the earth to pieces, given time enough and foliage and no opposition. There are limits to life, human and all else, no matter what we say or want. And when only a few can be born out of all who might be born, when deliberate or unwitting control of numbers is forced upon humanity by natural circumstances, choices must be made. First and foremost is the question of values. What do we value most in ourselves and others? The quality and dignity of the individual person, of whatever age and race, or a multiplicity of people no matter what sort of persons they may be? And apart from all of this is another question. Since every woman once a month starts an egg on the road toward development, at what point does any one of them have more right than another to continue on its way?

Laymen are inclined to distinguish between miscarriage and abortion, generally regarding termination of pregnancy during the first two or three months as miscarriage and later terminations as abortion. To the medical man and the biologist they are all abortions. And fortunately for most of them nature herself is responsible. Natural abortion usually follows when something is wrong with the egg, the fertilizing sperm, the process of uinon, the place and circumstance of implantation. Errors such as these are mostly self-eliminating during the first two weeks of pregnancy, and both the mistake and its erasure pass unsuspected. Yet the number is undoubtedly high, not less than a third of all conceptions. More is known concerning natural abortions that occur at some later stage when the event causes concern and usually medical examination. They occur in less than ten per cent of all pregnancies begun before the age of thirty, but after thirty years the frequency rises sharply to more than forty per cent, the likelihood increasing with increasing age. This should not be surprising. Human beings are remarkable, in fact unique, in their slow rate of maturing and their tenacity of life. With but few exceptions all other mammals of the same or very much greater size would die of old age during their third or fourth decade if living to old age were possible. Even humans are at their prime at twenty and age noticeably thereafter. Hence the questionable practice of always sending the cream of the masculine crop to fight and die in wars.

Unfortunately for some more or less humans-on-the-way, many that should have aborted naturally are maintained to full term. Once well rooted, so to speak, the organism continues to grow, but into what? Nature, that is, the developing or implanting egg within the womb, is a self-screening system up to a point. It is not prepared to cope with trouble that is not inborn, such as viral infection or drug effects. Nor is it prepared for any imprefection in the process of true twinning. So what to do with the limbless infant, the brainless body, the two-in-ones? Throughout human history until present times and throughout the hundred million years of development within the womb, the crippled and the witless died shortly after birth, unwanted and uncared for. Siamese conditions meant death of mother and offspring during the agony of delivery. Now there is no discrimination, except for the occasional merciful compassion of the delivering physician when privacy permits, and usually what can be born is born and kept alive. All but the marginal imbecilic are then institutionalized for as long as they live. And worse can happen, although a triumph of technological sophistication. Siamese twins joined head to head by skull top and brain were delivered by Caeserian section and maintained alive for two weeks. Given continuing care of the same sort they could have been kept alive indefinitely. If man must always do what he is capable of doing, for the satisfaction of his skill, we face a nightmare world.

If a human right exists at all it is the right to be born with normal body and mind, with the prospect of developing further to fulfillment. If this is to be denied, then life and consciousness are a mockery and a chance should be made for another throw of the ovarian dice. We are all born without permission, and no living being has the right to demand a living misery for another. And where no man has such a right, neither does church or state. No child must be born without a hope.

So where do we stand? For though the essential problem may remain the same, the timing of its solution can make all the difference. The law has too much to say. Once breath has been drawn, a life is a life, no matter what sort of life a complex assembly of flesh and bone may represent. In olden times everywhere and in parts of the world today when infant mortality eliminated a large percentage of every generation, a little more neglect than usual or even outright exposure took care of the situation. Now in our technological societies we can and usually do keep everything alive whether it is truly human or merely technically so. Euthanasia at either end of life, however greatly mercy calls for it, is legally hazardous and is likely to remain so. Perhaps we mistrust the doctors, or the responsibility may be too great. Yet double standards operate and we drop napalm indiscriminately on unseen targets elsewhere in the world. It is easier always, but not necessarily better, to get rid of an unwanted confrontation before it stares you in the face, and the sooner the better.

Suppose we take a particular but hypothetical situation such as a definite forecast of a German measles epidemic of unusual intensity due to strike a community in a few weeks' time. The wisest course for all young married women would be to avoid conception at all costs and by whatever means. The next would be to ensure that any fertilized egg be sent on its way to oblivion without becoming implanted in the womb. So far only the pill or the loop may have been involved, and the woman alone has been in control. Yet we are expecting too much, and the first alarm is usually realization of pregnancy at about the time of an exposure to the disease, during the first three months, when the embryo is most vulnerable to the viral attack. This is the time for evasive action, in other words, to abort. At this time it can easily and safely accomplished, and in a matter of weeks the woman can start all over again if she and her mate are so minded. Even though the embryo may or may not have been normal, no one was there, no person, no soul, but only the pospect of something. To continue the pregnancy under such a hazard is like Russian roulette—when the trigger is pulled the chamber may be empty and you survive, or it may not and out go your brains. The chance is too great.

Once the need for an abortion arises, the longer action is delayed the more difficult it becomes. In Sweden where abortion laws are very liberal it may still take as much as two months before an abortion is sanctioned. During that period the fetus can grow to a size too great for casual passage and surgery becomes necessary. Finally there comes a time when the fetus is termed viable, after about six months, when it has some slight prospect of living if removed from the womb. Then many questions arise that are better avoided. But if nothing is done and an infant is eventually born who is blind, deaf and mentally retarded, who takes care of it, what kind of person can develop, what anguish of frustration and self-imprisonment lie ahead? No amend can be made to either mother or child.

The human right is the right of every individual to be born without handicap in mind or body, to be nurtured in every way during infancy and childhood so that full development is achieved and to maintain the integrity of the person thereafter. If this is not a right, there is no other. And it is all of one piece. A right to be well born includes a right to grow to fruition, without violation of the person. What then are the rights of society to impose its will upon the individual? Only to ensure a peaceful coexistence and the maintenance of sustaining circumstances.

We are born unequal in every way except for the need for self-fulfillment, although this satisfaction must not be at others' expense. No man is good enough to be another man's master. Slavery is supposedly an outmoded state, but it persists in many forms under different names. Age compels youth to fight distant wars of policy far removed in fact and thought from defense of home. And for too long a time man has compelled woman to carry and bear a child whether she wanted to or not. Men have always held the reins of power, being physically the stronger of the sexes, and the enjoyment of power in some has known no bounds. But power is might, not right, and subtle tyranny is rampant. The laws prohibiting birth control by either contraception or abortion are all man-made, not woman-made, and so are all the reasons put forth for their creation. As a

noted medical scientist has said, "by what right does
state or church claim a jurisdiction superior to that of a
woman involved in pregnancy? For every woman should
be able to have an unwanted pregnancy aborted at her own
request, subject only to the consent of her husband and
the advice of her physician." Such a statement goes most
of the way to acknowledging the ancient right of a woman,
though it still leaves her subject to male authority. In spite
of present emancipation of women, however, both secular
and ecclesiastic law still implicitly regard them as chattel
and vehicle under the control of man.

Here is an experience of a young doctor in training:

I delivered my first baby. This is supposed to be one of the
most beautiful and poetic moments of existence for all concerned, yet no poetry comes; only a little mellow sadness, *triste
en France.* The beginning of a new life, infinity, and, if you
believe it, the birth of a soul. And yet, beauty was not there.

What feeling did I have?

A young boy is waiting to play ball and sees the first drop
of rain, and another, and another, until a flood results. Over-
population! An impossible wall of water washing over all human values, dissolving the essential freedom of human life by
crowding one too close to another.

But the mother in you and me must argue back. How simple
and pure the beauty of the love of mother and child; how
eternal the Greek statues of mothers with children in their
arms. How basic a symbol for religion and selfless love the
Madonna and Christ child.

A young girl of twenty. Alone. Her second child with no
father. She was thin and frightened, almost too ashamed to feel

pain and too apologetic to complain of it. No one waited for the child. No shriek of elation from the waiting room; nothing but the whirring of the air-conditioning system, a testimonial to the substitution by modern man of comfort for all else.

But I behave as a technician. All I need do is aspirate, tie, and cut the cord, sew up those skin tears in the mother, and forget the others. All I need are white gowns and asepsis, and I can walk away and pretend I didn't notice the tragedy.

Forcing a woman, whether married or not, to bear a child against her will is as great an invasion of privacy and a potential destruction of the person as sending a reluctant draftee abroad to kill or be killed. No matter how great the justification may be or may seem to be the individual is no longer a person but a means to an end. However this may be, what is the origin of the present prohibitions concerning birth control, with their savage penalties in the case of abortion? Surprisingly, we are coping not with cruel medieval attitudes but with harsh laws laid down by our much more recent mid-Victorian predecessors. Until then the general rule was that of the ancient Greeks. Aristotle, who recommended abortion when couples already have children in excess, stated that life did not begin until "quickening" and so abortion was permissible during the preceding months. More precisely, abortion was allowable during the first forty days for a male infant and eighty days for females. How anyone could know the sex of the fetus at such an early stage we are not told. But this forty-day, eighty-day rule was preserved in the Justinian code a thousand years after Aristotle, and it has survived until recent times. Undoubtedly the abortive procedures were extremely dangerous, as much so as in the worst circumstances of fly-by-night illegal abortions of our present time. However, medieval English comon law permitted abortion on demand provided it was accomplished before quickening. The pregnant woman, even if married, was the sole person whose consent or request was required. This remained the law of England until 1803 and was the common law of New York until 1830. Even then the new laws merely distinguished between an abortion before and after quickening. Not until 1861 did England pass legislation without respect to the time of gestation, with similar American legislation following shortly after. And so also with the the Roman Catholic Church. Except for the short reign of Pope Sixtus V, from 1585 to 1590, when all abortions were banned, the Aristotelian forty-day, eighty-day rule was accepted throughout the long history of the Church until 1869. Obviously what is right or wrong has undergone shifts and changes in both church and state and there is no reason why the rulings of our grandfathers, great or not, should be respected more than those of other men in other times. Laws are generally made to express the bias and to serve the interests of ruling classes of any particular age. In the mid-nineteenth century the need was felt for large families to fuel the industrial revolution, and at a time when sex and sin were synonymous the price had to be paid. Economic interest and moral fervor went hand in hand.

An unwanted pregnancy is an assault upon the person, whether she is married or not, and living with it is so onerous that many women risk death through illegal abortion rather than suffer its far-reaching effects. The sexual urge is notoriously difficult to control, and there is no time when a couple can be sure of maintaining a levelheaded foresight in their sexual relationship. Yet man makes the laws, and women take the consequences.

The risk of pregnancy is greatest among those who are least prepared for it physically, emotionally or maternally. They are the young who attain sexual maturity without realizing what is involved and who are likely to be incapable of producing a normal infant. They are the neurotic, with bad or broken marriages, who take risks and go through pregnancy in a state of harmful emotional stress. And they are the older women in menopause who think that at last they are safe, but become pregnant and are the most likely to produce a mongolian infant.

Altogether between 1,000,000 and 2,000,000 women undergo illegal abortion every year in the United States, with about 4,000 deaths. It is estimated that about 800,000 abortions, ninety-nine per cent of them illegal, are performed on married women who already are mothers of two or more children. A generation ago about seven out of a thousand high school girls had a baby out of wedlock. Now the rate is seventeen per thousand, amounting to a total of about 100,000 per year. Probably another 200,000 undergo illegal abortion or make the attempt to induce it themselves. The death rate for unmarried women is four times as high as for married women, at least sixty per cent of it the result of illegal abortions. When need is so great, no law can be effective and only forces the practice into a deadly hole in the corner. Women are being driven alone and afraid into a dangerous underworld or the equally dangerous practice of self-induced abortion.

Yet the tide is turning. Old prohibitions weaken and fall before the flood of new opinion. Slowly state after state passes or considers liberalized abortion laws. In the United States the code approved by the American Medical Association and the American Law Institute is being followed, namely, an abortion is permissible if continued pregnancy would impair the physical or mental health of the mother; if there is risk that a child might be born physically or mentally defective; or if the pregnancy results from either incest or rape. The new abortion law in Britain goes further and includes the mental health of other children in the family. Yet the most liberal laws, such as those of Britain and Scandinavia, are still restrictive and involve delays. So even in Scandinavia many women go to Poland where they can get an abortion on demand. At the best, then, it is no easy matter to obtain an abortion quickly, however great the need.

Hopefully the answer to the problem, apart from a general liberalization of the abortion laws, lies in the private domain, although reinforced by public education. Young people need to be fully informed about themselves as warm-blooded mammalian creatures inhabiting this planet, with emphasis on their burgeoning reproductive nature. Sex education should be mandatory in all high schools, public or otherwise, and presented as thoroughly as now given in the schools of Denmark. We prepare young men for war. We should prepare young women especially for what inevitably lies ahead for them. In the uncertain future all ignorance is hazardous, no situation can be fully prepared for, and the best we can do is to launch each new generation as well equipped mentally as possible to cope with life as it comes. Old rules will not suffice in a rapidly changing world. Sexual life will continue to be set free from reproduction, and the means of birth control will become ever simpler and more effective. The Swedish M-pill already shows the way. No woman using it would even know whether she was pregnant, would have no need for any soul-searching and would never have to undergo surgery for an unwanted pregnancy even if the law allowed. Whether this particular pill works well or not, better kinds are sure to come, and sex life in Western societies may recover its ancient spontaneity.

CHAPTER 14 *People and Persons*

Good seed needs good soil. Genetics apart, the hope of the future depends on the quality of individuals, as whole persons sound in mind and body, compassionate, creative, intelligent and courageous. Full development depends on a balanced nourishment of the growing body and brain, on more than adequate love at crucial times, on continuous enrichment of the mind through all the senses, on using the mind in contemplation, analysis and comprehension, on developing and keeping the sense of wonder, and exercising body and mind together in action. Such is the joy of living. It begins at birth and may last as long as life. This is man triumphant, newly formed on a aging planet. In the dawning age of man on earth, man at his best is magnificent. But success breeds more success, and too much of anything can be bad for all.

This planet can grow a living crop of a certain size depending on total resources of space, light and raw materials. Throughout all the ages the crop has been exceedingly diversified, and its composition has changed continually with the passage of time. But all has been in balance until the last few thousand years. Now for the first time in the history of creation one single kind has taken over, pushing all else to the brink of oblivion except what is grist to its own well-being. The human crop, like any other, is self-propagating, but the checks and balances that used to hold sway are no longer in control. Mankind is on an expansive rampage with no end in sight. This is the ultimate threat to the nature of human beings, at least within the foreseeable future.

This future in fact is already upon us, and changes continue that intensify the problem. As a whole mankind is breeding at a rate far greater than is needed for replacement from one generation to the next. And there is a notable tendency for people to move to large centers where population density is greatest. More people everywhere, older people everywhere and jostling crowds in adjoining cities form the contemporary scene. Even in the most affluent country in the world, the United States, where space still abounds, the population increase and the migration of people have necessitated greater restrictions on individual behavior, crowded schools and recreation areas, vanishing countryside, air and water pollution, endless traffic jams and a steady loss in time, solitude, quiet, beauty and peace of mind. And much of what is already lost is lost forever. So speaks a leading demographer. Such is already the state of affairs. What will it be like by the end of this century, when our children are parents or grandparents, when there are twice as many people? The stress of too many bodies moving too close together, the impoverished environment where little is seen except walls and roads and faces, and a chronic shortage of essential components of food will impair the development of human beings from their inception to the end of individual time.

Mankind is already one, a large bursting family bickering in turmoil within the limits of its house, with some rooms more densely packed and the inhabitants more undernourished than others. We do not have far to look to see what may lie ahead for all. The Indian state of West Bengal has reached the saturation point. Conditions there are as if you took all of the thirty million poor of the United States, crammed them into the state of Maine, and gave each individual a daily food ration of a handful of rice. That is not the sort of life we are here for. What hope exists for any person to develop to fruition under circumstances like this?

Much of mankind lives on rice, but rice alone no more than bread alone suffices to make a man. Protein is essential. As long as a child can suckle at the breast, which may be for two or more years in parts of Asia and Africa, and the milk supply is enough, protein deficiency is not serious. Yet protein starvation is the lot of millions, and the children are the most vulnerable. A former food minister of the government of India, speaking to the Committee on the World Food Crisis made the following statement:

It has been estimated that between thirty and forty per cent of the children of India have suffered permanent brain damage by the time they reach school age because of protein deficiency.

This means that we are, in effect, producing subhuman beings at the rate of thirty-five million a year. By the time they reach school age they are unable to concentrate sufficiently to absorb and retain knowledge. So to this extent it might be said that the millions of rupees spent on new school buildings and facilities have been wasted.

Protein is essential to all growth, and especially for normal brain development from an early stage in the womb until final elaboration of brain organization is attained, which is around the age of six. In this connection maternal diet and infant and child diet are vital to the full development of the potential. Protein deficiency can wreak havoc even where adequate food is available, for in Western society young mothers, concerned with watching their figures and insufficiently aware of the importance of protein, may voluntarily restrict their diet to too great an extent; babies born weighing less than five and one-half pounds at birth suffer more brain damage, mental retardation and survival problems. The same threat holds wherever regional poverty, whether in cities or country, reduces protein and vitamin intake below a critical level. Yet over much of the world, especially in the warmer lands, a protein shortage afflicts all mankind. Undoubtedly the world food supply can be improved, both in quantity and quality, though we devastate the planet in other ways in doing so. But at best we will be hard put to sustain a population of the present size if each member is to receive the proper nourishment his body requires.

Unfortunately this is not the prospect. We are in the late stages of a population explosion. As public health procedures have spread from country to country and industrialization has increased the means of support, a greater and greater percentage of those who get born live on to maturity, reproduction and their own old age. Birth rates are no longer balanced by death rates, and each individual now clutters up the planet for several times as long as was usual in the past. Half a million years ago there were perhaps half a million human beings, probably less, living precariously as hunters and food gatherers. Ages passed before the 250-million level was reached, at about the time of Christ. Another sixteen centuries passed before it became 500 million, then two more to reach 1 billion, by 1850. Now it is already 3⅓ billion and the population will reach 7 billion by the turn of the century if the present rate of increase is maintained. In 1900 mankind increased by 40,000 persons per day. Now the daily increase is 180,000. Forty per cent of those alive today are under fifteen years of age, and in another ten years they will be parents. Only in the most industrialized, predominantly white societies has the rate of increase already fallen, and even so in the United States the present 200 million population will be 380 million in thirty-five years if no further change occurs. On and on it goes, with people, people everywhere and not a face to please.

The problem of people, who are not statistics but individual persons, varies greatly in this rapidly changing world. A particular problem for the intolerant whites is that already eighty per cent of the world population is colored, and the rate of increase of the colored races far outstrips the rest. In the long run, as the diversity of people becomes generally accepted and admired, a degree of warmth may flush the paler faces. Meanwhile the greater problems persist. One is the gap between the rich and the poor. There are less than a billion people in the rich countries of the northern hemisphere, but more than two billion in the poorer southern countries. And the average wealth is fifteen times as great in the rich as in the poor, with the gap widening steadily year by year. That the rich should support the poor is inevitable, for the world's richest people, those of the United States, already consume half the world's annual production of nonrenewable resources. It takes a lot of Asians or Africans or South Americans at their material levels of living to consume as much as one American at his. It is important to remember that the high and rising populations of the poorer countries are not owing to any large increase in birth rate but are mainly caused by a large decrease in death rate as a result of the importation of modern medicine from the north. In the industrial revolution in the northern countries wealth came first and health followed after. In the southern countries health has come first but the necessary extra wealth is still not there. Consequently the individuals constituting the swelling populations of the poorer lands are in large part chronically undernourished throughout prenatal and postnatal life, handicapped physically and mentally from the start however good their genes may be.

Mankind everywhere now sees the precipice ahead. Fitfully and all too slowly the brakes are being applied. Sooner or later in all countries the population must become stabilized, but the present momentum is such that we would be lucky to level out at less than 10 billion people. Whether more or less, a leveling is bound to occur, for the alternative leads to impossibly absurd conditions. Given another seven centuries of the present rate of increase, there would be literally standing room only on the earth. Population control is urgent, and by all rational means. Nature's means as applied or experienced by man, namely, war, pestilence and famine, have worked only temporarily in the past, and something much more effective as well as less brutal is required. Already there is an International Planned Parenthood Federation, a recent meeting of which had twelve hundred delegates from eighty-five countries. The need is recognized, but the task is great. Intrauterine contraceptive devices and hormone pills are being widely distributed and exert some effect. In India a program of extensive male sterilization, a simple and reversible operation, is also underway. Japan, with limited space and no place to go, has cut its birth rate in half in less than a decade by employing all such methods and abortion, too. Contraception alone, however, cannot do the job. People must want fewer children. Reproduction, although a private act, has widespread social consequences and is not a private affair. In the past a couple may have had freedom to produce as many children as they wanted, but there is no right. What comes first is the quality of what is born, the prospects of growth and health, and accommodation of number to the conditions of life on earth.

Man is the latest notable product of several billion years of evolutinoary creation on this planet. Apart from the last few thousand years the emphasis throughout has been on quality of the individual, for upon this all else depends. Throughout most of his subhuman and early human history man has been a struggling, blossoming but far from dominant being, thinly scattered over certain regions of the earth. He was man in all his glory ten thousand years ago as a hunter and artist. He was no less a little later, in the early days of settled communities, when he first took hold of his environment, became an agriculturist, domesticated animals, discovered irrigation, the wheel and how to smelt. Nor has any age matched in thought and appreciation of beauty the glory that was Greece. Yet in terms of numbers, only a fraction of what now encumbers the land. Multiplication beyond the need for survival of the species as a healthy component of the earth's frail life has little value and simply expresses the latent capacity of all living things whenever opportunity presents.

Mankind as such is in the process of coming of age and of becoming for the first time in all history a single, worldwide community of beings. Growth and maturation have come unevenly, and turmoil and tension is everywhere. If there is a road to the future at all it is a narrow one that no thundering herd of neurotic, substandard human beings can pass along. Sooner or later we will bring our numbers into balance with what the earth can support when all the nonrenewable capital of natural resources is gone and only the basic annuity remains. This is the shape of things to come, and the time is closer than we think. When the plundering of the planet comes to an end for lack of plunder, perhaps we will restore what may still be possible of the living world that once was spacious, stimulating and lovely. Otherwise what hope is left for all those persons yet to come in the long ages that lie ahead? We are in need of all our individual and collective wisdom to find the course.

Peaceful coexistence and the adjustment of population size to the circumstances of this lovely earth are merely the conditions for a long-term future. In the end as always we come to the nature of the individual, the human person. The essence of man is his humanity, with all that that entails. There is already a great debate concerning the control of human nature. Man the farmer, the miner and the civil engineer have gone far in messing up the earth. Now man the biological engineer has an itch to get his finger in the works. Knowledge is power. Not necessarily to produce what one wants but to do something that results in change. So there is enlightenment and a growing sense of power in being able to rear embryos to some extent in test tubes, to transplant embryos from one individual or species to another, to break the genetic code and to induce mutations at will, to store reproductive cells deep frozen for future use, and not least in the beginning efforts to create life itself. Man is said to have been created in the image of God. This is wishful thinking, yet the feeling is there, and we are acting as though it were more than image. There is modern magic in speaking of genes, DNA and double helixes. Yet man in the robes of his Creator may be the ultimate threat to his own essential being, for power is always arrogant and imperfectly informed. We should leave well alone, even in thought, this matter of playing with our own constitution, for taking the long perspective, it all amounts to monkey business performed by emancipated but meddling-fingered curiosity-ridden beings whose ancestral past is all too clear. We have long had the means and we now have the need to concentrate on the quality and fulfillment of the human person as he now can be and to cultivate the human garden for its finest flowers. We can do it if we will.

Bibliography

Man's Emerging Mind. N. J. Berrill. Dodd, Mead & Co. 1955. Apollo Editions 1961.

Sex and the Nature of Things. N. J. Berrill. Dodd, Mead & Co. 1953. Apollo Editions 1964.

The Empty Fortress. B. Betelman. Free Press. 1967.

Ourselves Unborn. G. W. Corner Yale University Press. 1944.

Too Many Americans. L. Day and A. Day. Houghton, Mifflin Co. 1964.

Birth Control in the Modern World. E. Draper. Penguin Book Co. 1965.

The First Nine Months. G. L. Flanagan. Simon and Shuster. 1962.

Science and the Safe Period. C. G. Hartman. Williams and Wilkins. 1962.

How Children Learn. J. Holt. Pitman. 1967.

The Control of Fertility. G. Pincus. Academic Press. 1965.

The Crucial Years from Birth to Six. Maya Pines. Harper & Row. 1967.

You are Extraordinary. R. Williams. Random House. 1967.

Nutrition in a Nutshell. R. Williams. Doubleday & Co. (Dolphin Edition). 1962.

Index

Index

Hemophilia, 91-92, 114
Hens, *see* Chickens
Hermaphrodites, 75
Hormones, 21, 27-30, 33, 61-63, 77-80, 87, 94, 122, 128-129
Horses, 59
Huntington's chorea, 91
Huxley, Aldous, quoted, 6-7
Hydrocephalus, 91

Implantation process, 37-41, 67, 68
Inbreeding, 90
Individual differences, 3-4, 71, 84-88, 146-147
Infant mortality, 95, 131, 153
Infanticide, 25
Infertility, 17, 21-23, 30
Inguinal canals, 57
Inheritance, 71, 81-96
    artificial insemination and, 23
    biparental, 14
Insemination, artificial, 23-24
Institute for Learning Disability, 142
Institute for Neurological Organization, 141
Insulin, 120
International Planned Parenthood Federation, 168
Intrauterine device, *see* Loop, the
Intrauterine surgery, 117
Iodides, 112
IUD, *see* Loop, the

James, William, 134
Jaundice, prenatal, 112

Labor, 129-132
Lanugo, 56
Loop, the (IUD), 31-32
LSD, 99

Mammals, 12-14, 16-17, 51, 55, 56, 59, 67, 97, 123, 151
Maternal mortality, 94, 95
Measles, 103-104, 127, 144, 153
Menopause, 26
Menstruation, 32-33
Menstruation pill, 32-34, 161
Mental retardation, 90, 95, 103, 108, 117-119, 141
Metabolism, 86, 89, 118-121
Mice, 12, 15, 36, 39, 40, 67, 79, 105, 123
Milk glands, 56-57, 129
Milton, John, quoted, 10
Miscarriages, 94, 95, 123, 151
Mongoloids, 95-96, 159
Monkeys, 36, 59, 106, 112, 114, 137
Morning-after pill, 32, 33
Mother-infant relationship, 137-139
M-pill, *see* Menstruation pill
Mumps, 103, 106, 127
Mustard gas, 99
Mutations, 98

National Institute of Neurological Diseases and Blindness, 118
Navel, 44, 130
Nidation, 37
Night blindness, congenital, 91
Notochord, 50

Octuplets, 62
Open split spinal column, 91
"Orienting reflex," 136
Ovaries, 7, 12, 15, 17, 19, 20, 21, 38, 40, 47, 57, 60-62, 64, 72, 77, 78, 96, 97, 128
Oviduct, 38, 53
Ovum, *see* Eggs

Papal Study Commission on Birth Control, 34

Index